ADVAN

NURSING SCHOOL: WHAT I LEARNED MAY MAKE YOUR LIFE EASIER!

"*Nursing School: What I Learned May Make Your Life Easier!* by Talonda Rogers, MSN, RN, is an excellent book written about a topic that is often overlooked, but desperately needs to be addressed. It gives a realist view of the struggles nursing students experience both inside and outside of the classroom. It is packed with practical ways to facilitate a nursing student's success. The suggestions are holistic, encompassing physical, psychosocial, economic, and spiritual areas. Although the focus is nursing students, the information can be applied to many other rigorous academic programs as well as the general well-being of those not enrolled in school. So many times, we incorrectly believe that students innately know how to succeed; this book gives them the tools not only to pass, but to thrive. I would highly recommend this book to anyone considering an education in nursing."

—Michele R. Carpenter, MSN, RN, Nurse Educator

"Beautifully written and highly encouraging. Talonda opens her book by giving her readers a glimpse of her personal struggles. She then maps out a step-by-step guide that enables the nursing student success from start to finish. This awe-inspiring book is a tool for every nursing student."

—L'Tanya Taylor, MSN, RN

"Throughout this text, Talonda Rogers gives tangible tips on how to succeed in nursing school, along with personal stories about becoming a nurse. She outlines the different levels of nursing, and the process involved in becoming a nurse to help her audience explore if nursing should be a career choice. The book is loaded with resources nursing students will find useful to succeed in his or her nursing school path. If you or someone you know is interested in a nursing career, I encourage you to read this book. It will help determine if nursing is for you, and assist in making the nursing school journey a little less challenging. Every nursing student should have a copy of this book as a valuable resource to navigate their way through nursing school."

—Kathy Blaize, MSN, RN

"Talonda presents a compelling discussion about the benefits of a career in nursing while providing students with a roadmap for success when starting nursing school!"

—Nancy K. Haughton, MSN, RN,
Director of Practical Nursing, Chester County
Intermediate Unit Practical Nursing Program

"I found this book to be an easy read almost right away. It kept me interested, as it was written from the standpoint of an individual who, though well educated, speaks plainly and very clearly. There are times when Talonda Rogers is humorous at the same time she's making a point, keeping you interested. On the technical aspects of the read, she is spot on in her suggestions and knowledge of what a student will undoubtedly go through while getting their degree. She covers everything from her own history and why she chose to go to nursing school to what to do with that nursing education. I only wish that I had this book as a primary source of my education. I feel it would have been an enormous help in knowing what was to come as opposed to learning on the fly. I enthusiastically recommend this read to anyone contemplating a calling/career in nursing."

—Willard N. Carpenter, LPN, Retired,
Author, Writer, "One of the Men of Amish Fiction,"
Journalist, The Boyertown Bulletin

Nursing School

Nursing School

What I Learned May
Make Your Life Easier!

TALONDA S. ROGERS, MSN, RN

NURSING SCHOOL
Published by Purposely Created Publishing Group™

Printed in the United States of America

ISBN: 978-1-64484-293-5

Special discounts are available on bulk quantity purchases by book clubs, associations and special interest groups.
For details email: sales@publishyourgift.com or call (888) 949-6228.
For information logon to: www.PublishYourGift.com

DEDICATION

To my husband and children, Robert, Sabria, Tayah, Rena, and Cameron. For all the nights and days, you watched me toil, for all the times you waited for me to join you, for all the times you wondered if mom would stop being a crazy mom, for all the ways you loved me through my journey.

This book is dedicated to you! If I had to memorialize this moment in a song, it would be

"Because You Loved Me" by Celine Dion.

~Mom~

TABLE OF CONTENTS

PREFACE

As far back as I can remember, I always said I wanted to be a nurse. But when I got to the twelfth grade, I decided to enter college as a chemistry major instead. I know you must be thinking, "If you wanted to be a nurse, then why would you go to college for something else?" Well, you see, I was talked out of being a nurse by well-meaning family members who thought they were doing me a favor by trying to spare me trouble and point me to a career choice that they thought was better for me. I was told that I wasn't strong enough, emotionally and mentally, to become a nurse. "You? Be a nurse? How are you going to be a nurse when you can't stand the sight of blood?" Because that was said to me, I began to doubt if nursing was really the career for me. Would I succeed? Because after all, I am squeamish, and I can't stand the sight of blood! I thought since my family knows me best, they must be right. "You look like a businesswoman. I always imagined you as a businesswoman," said a cousin. Someone else suggested I go to school to be a pharmacist because they make "good money." In order to be a pharmacist, I was told that I needed to declare chemistry as my major. With doubt now firmly at work in me, I set out to college with chemistry as my major.

I was mixed up and confused, not knowing what I wanted to do because it was more important to please other people than to follow my own heart. Or should I say, it was about fulfilling a need in me that craved acceptance from people, for people to be proud of me, for people to see me as doing a great thing, being important and accomplished.

I grew up in a house that was multigenerational that included my grandmother, the matriarch of our family, my mother, an uncle, sisters, and cousins. Yes, we had a big house. It was great for having someone to play with but not so great for getting individualized attention. My mom worked very hard and often into the night. If I wanted to see her, I had to wait up for her. I didn't have a lot of her attention or the attention of my father.

My father and mother split up when I was very young. I didn't see him that often, but when I did, I really cherished those times. I often think that achieving more and more over the years was really about me getting my mother's and father's attention and approval. I think subconsciously I needed to hear them say, "Good job" or "I'm proud of you." They do say those encouraging words, and they do see what I'm doing, and I know they are very proud of me. We butt heads a lot when I was growing up, but it's worked itself out. That came with maturity. As I approach middle age, I see them and love them for who they are. Parenting is hard. There are no manuals that tell you how to do it. That's why God created grandmothers.

I had two strong and wise grandmothers. I was closer to one of them than the other because of distance. My grandmother, Delores also known as Dee, who raised me will forever be the strongest woman I will ever know. May she rest in heavenly peace. If it were not for her, I don't know where anyone in my family would be today.

Back to my college story. It was important for me to attend college no matter what my major was because before I went to school, there weren't many people in my family with college degrees. I believe only my uncle and an older cousin went to college and finished.

When I got to college as a chemistry major, guess what happened. "What?" you ask. I failed not one but two classes and ended up on academic probation. Me, an honor graduate! On academic probation! How did that happen? Not me! I'm a good student! Well, I'll tell you how it happened. My heart wasn't in it. I had no clue what I was doing in chemistry, and I hated going to class. I skipped a few classes because of that fact. Hey, my parents certainly weren't there to make me go. Adopting that mentality, I got behind and even more lost in the coursework than I could have imagined. That's enough to fail a couple of classes.

After deciding that I no longer wanted to major in chemistry, my major became "undeclared." Undeclared means you don't know what you want to do, and you won't have a "declared" major until you figure it out. After a couple of semesters and going to summer school to catch up and pull up my grade point average (GPA), I completed my general education requirements.

What did I do next? Glad you asked. I decided to follow what my cousin wanted me to do. Yes, I declared business as my major. Clearly, I would do well because after all "I look like a businesswoman." I ended up completing college with a degree in business. I received my bachelor of science in marketing in the spring of 1997. I landed a couple of different positions in business and then got a job in marketing. I was excited! Surely, this was all paying off because I landed a job in the actual field I went to school for. Life was getting real.

I started working in the marketing department for an investment firm. Guess what? It wasn't what I expected or even what I wanted. I was bored everyday! I was certain life had more to offer me than just sitting in a cubicle for nine hours a day (one hour for lunch), looking at and creating proposals for the salespeople and keeping the inventory room stocked. I was miserable. I thought about the days when I was young and talked about going to nursing school. I knew I had so much more to offer the world than what I was. Then I got pregnant; this was my second pregnancy. Since I was deemed high risk, I was put on bedrest, and boy was I happy because I had already made up my mind that I wasn't going back to that boring job.

I just mentioned that this was my second pregnancy. Eighteen months before, I lost my firstborn, a son, the son I always prayed for. The son I desperately wanted was stillborn at forty weeks, a full-term stillborn. Although there was never an official cause of death, per the autopsy, I suspect it was the undetected gestational diabetes that caused me to lose him. I had every symptom of gestational diabetes. I was a classic textbook case with increased hunger, thirst, and urination. To this day, I still don't understand *how* it was missed, but it was, and I have accepted that.

It took me a while to come to acceptance. Acceptance doesn't mean that I have forgotten; it just means that I have released myself from blame. I attribute my sanity about the situation to my faith in God. I firmly believe that only God could help me through the most devastating calamity of my life, burying my child.

Rewind to a few weeks before my devastation, I was put on bedrest to help stop the pre-term labor contractions I was having because it was too early to deliver my baby. I had the standard Glucose Tolerance Test (GTT) at twenty-five weeks like every woman who gets that far along in her pregnancy. That test came back "abnormal." As a result of that abnormal test, I had to go back to the doctor for a three-hour GTT. That test came back "normal." However, in the weeks approaching forty weeks, I developed symptoms of diabetes. I had blurred vision, increased thirst, increased urination, and weight loss. The home visiting nurse found glucose (sugar) and protein in my urine, all of which we reported to the doctor's office. That was on a Friday. I was told by the office staff that my doctor was on vacation, but since I had an upcoming appointment on Tuesday, they'd see me then. Looking back on this incident, I should have questioned this reasoning and demanded to see a doctor. This being my first pregnancy and not knowing how to advocate for myself became the source of a lot of guilt after the devastating outcome of my pregnancy. Hindsight sure is 20/20.

I had always been a scheduled C-section. My date was planned, and I couldn't wait for the day of his birth to arrive. On the morning of my scheduled C-section, I got out of bed with excitement about what my future held. I was finally going to meet the baby I had been waiting for. Although I had chosen not to find out the sex of my unborn child, I knew in my heart he was a boy the entire time. Upon arrival at the hospital, getting settled and connected to the baby monitoring equipment, the nursing staff had trouble obtaining a fetal heart rate. I say trouble because nurse after nurse entered and then left my room to get another nurse to help locate the heart rate. They thought they got a fetal heart rate, but in retrospect, it was just mine because the rate was too low to be my baby's. The heart rate was in the eighties, which is a standard adult heart rate, whereas a fetal heart rate is in the range of 120-160 beats per minute. They even brought in an apparatus that resembled an automated external defibrillator (AED) that was placed on my enlarged abdomen. After placing it on my abdomen, they fired it in order to "wake up" (their words, not mine) my baby because sometimes they are "asleep." At the time, I was not a nurse, yet even I could spot this as shady information, and I became upset. The nurses tried to comfort me, stating that sometimes babies are just "sleeping." By the way, after being shocked, my baby didn't wake up. Still in light of this assessment information, there was no sense of urgency to get me to the operating room (OR) any earlier than the scheduled 11:30 a.m. C-section. The anesthesiologist strolled into my room very nonchalantly with a cup of coffee around 11:00 a.m. to complete his questionnaire and get my consent for the surgery. At the strike of 11:30 a.m., I was wheeled into the OR to finally meet my baby. Devastation! I could hear a pin drop in the OR because none of the OR staff said a word as they delivered my baby and subsequently stitched me up. I did, however, hear CPR being performed in the room. My heart already knew the inevitable.

After he was born, I was very sick, almost near death myself, with a blood sugar of 750. Yes, people have died with much lower blood sugar numbers. In fact, I questioned why God would take my son and leave me here. I stayed in the hospital for eight days. Not only had I just had a Cesarean section, a major abdominal surgery, but I also had a nasogastric tube (NGT) for a couple of days. I only had the tube a couple of days because I pulled it out; I couldn't take it anymore. I was sick of being sick. I got myself all set to leave on the seventh day, and then the doctors decided that I was a diabetic because my blood sugars still remained high. But I wasn't a true diabetic then, and I'm not now. It was because they had just spent a week pumping my body full of fluids, some with sugar, because at one point I wasn't eating anything by mouth. On the seventh night, they wanted me to stay for one more night of observation for my condition. Mentally, I was through! I think the gravity of everything I had just experienced from losing my first child to the traumatic ordeal of having a tube inserted into my nose, down my throat, and into my stomach to having to plan my child's funeral while hospitalized was all too much. I was left with many unanswered questions. Why did this happen to me and my baby? How could this happen to me and my baby? How could he die? I thought I had done everything right. What did I do wrong? What went wrong? I thought to myself, "I am married. I have good insurance. I kept all of my appointments." I replayed these thoughts and questions over and over again in my mind for a long time.

My doctor let me know that if I got pregnant again, I would be considered high-risk, and if pre-term labor happened again, I would need to go on bedrest.

Fast forward to one and a half years later when I got pregnant again. I reached seven months into my pregnancy; I was ecstatic to go out on bedrest to get away from that boring job at the investment firm.

In light of what happened a year and a half prior, I was now considered to have a high-risk pregnancy. I was happy to have maternal fetal medicine doctors as well as a new OBGYN taking good care of me. Instead of only having a GTT done at twenty-five weeks, which came back "normal," my doctors decided to test me after thirty-three weeks. That test came back "abnormal." I had gestational diabetes and was immediately started on insulin. I had to check my blood sugar four times a day and report my numbers weekly. I was connected with a nutritionist as well. I stayed on bedrest until it was time to deliver my child. She was delivered two weeks early via Cesarean section because the results of an amniocentesis showed the umbilical cord wrapped around her neck. My doctors decided we needed to do the C-section the next day and gave me a steroid injection to help mature my baby's lungs since she was going to be born a bit early.

I always knew I would need a Cesarean section because when I was twenty-two-years-old, I had a surgery that removed eight fibroid tumors from my uterus. The area in which they were removed could cause me to have a uterine rupture if I ever went into natural labor. Therefore, I would always need to have a C-section to deliver any babies.

The day of the C-section, I was a complete wreck because I had gotten this far with my first pregnancy only to have a devastating outcome. The surgery did not take that long, and it was a success. I had spent nine months worrying about delivering a *live* baby because I never knew the reasons for losing my son. I was a nervous wreck all nine months. With her birth, the world was made right again. A huge feeling of relief came over me. I couldn't believe it. I was a mother! I gave birth to a healthy eight-pound, seven-ounce beautiful baby girl with a lot of hair. I felt so joyous and loved by God.

When I got pregnant with my third child a few months later, I was given a GTT at twelve weeks. The test was "normal." I had a second GTT test at the usual twenty-five weeks gestation, which came back "normal." I had a third GTT after thirty-three weeks; that test came back "abnormal." Again, here I was checking my blood sugar several times a day and giving myself insulin. One year and one day after my first daughter's birth came my second beautiful baby girl weighing in at seven pounds and thirteen ounces. Yes, that's right—366 days later, I gave birth to another baby. I felt like I was pregnant for two whole years. My husband and I decided that because daycare was so expensive that it would be better for me to be a stay-at-home mother because most of my income would most likely go to pay for daycare costs. I decided to stay at home until my children were old enough for school. In those years of being home, I thought to myself, "Why not go back to school to be what you always said you wanted to be?" A nurse!

So. that's exactly what I did. In the fall of 2007, I began a program to become a Licensed Practical Nurse. I graduated in December of 2008, passed my National Council Licensure Examination (NCLEX) in March of 2009, and that began my career as a nurse. Since then, I haven't looked back. My first position was in long-term care (nursing home). I worked for four and a half years as an LPN before returning to school to get my associate of science in nursing (ASN). Again, I took and passed my National Licensure Examination in July 2013 to become a registered nurse (RN). I worked for a while longer in long-term care as an RN before changing settings to acute care (hospital). At the hospital, the project I created for my nurse residency program gained recognition from those in powerful positions. I came up with a method to help decrease surgical site infections in patients who had just had surgery. Decreasing surgical site infections is a worldwide initiative as they cost billions of dollars each year to fight and treat. While working for the hospital, I was able to complete my coursework toward receiving my bachelor of science in nursing (BSN) in December of 2015. I began classes right away in January of 2016 toward completing my master of science in nursing. I gained a love for teaching students while working at the hospital. Many days, I was the primary nurse for the students whose nursing program used our hospital for training. We were a teaching hospital. In fact, it was the same hospital my program used when I went back to school to get my ASN. I remembered how I felt being a student, the nervousness, the doubt, the fear that plagues the mind, and the sleepless nights as I made sure I was prepared for the clinical day. Remembering where I came from, knowing that students need good teachers, knowing that there is a shortage of nurses and that it is largely due to a shortage of nurse educators are all reasons why I decided to go back to school yet again to get my master's in order to become a nurse educator.

Realizing how much focus my program required, I once again made the switch in healthcare settings to home health. I loved working with just one patient and the experience I gained with this new setting. I had the pleasure of working with a child, a very special, very bright little girl who stole my heart with her smile and ability to rise above all the challenges thrown at her because of the genetic condition she battled daily. It was a complete blessing to work with her and her family. It's rare to find such a great match in home health. I was fortunate.

Since getting my master's, I landed a teaching position with the very program that started my nursing career. I am a nursing instructor for the Licensed Practical Nursing Program, now known as the Practical Nursing Program (PNP) that I started with as a student back in 2007. My life feels like it has come full circle. I love teaching.

I am also a business owner of RISCQ by TALONDA Healthcare Consultants & Educators, LLC. RISCQ by TALONDA stands for Relate, Inspire, Serve, Care, & Quality by Teaching Actionable Lessons on New Diversity Appreciation.

The main focus of my company is to help decrease healthcare disparities in the United States through education. I educate students, medical professionals, other educators, and the community about the importance of being culturally competent in healthcare. I do this through in person seminars, trainings, and speaking engagements. Another focus of my company is educating nursing students through tutoring services to help them pass the NCLEX and regular unit exams. I offer pre-nursing courses to help students succeed once they begin a nursing program. I am also still involved with home health, seeing a select number of patients.

To learn more about my company and what services we offer, please visit my website at www.riscqhealthcare.com. You can also visit my other social media sites linked to my website.

INTRODUCTION

I like to start off by asking new nursing students, "What's your why?" I then go around the class and ask each student to state their reason. The last thing I do is pass out a picture of a stethoscope in the shape of a heart and ask them to write their reason on the inside of the heart and keep it with them in a place where they will easily see it every day. I ask students to do this because there will be days when you will need to remember your reason for deciding to go to nursing school. You will look down at that reason, and that reason will be staring back up at you through the worn plastic on the front of your binder. You will remember that your reasons are good. Your reasons are worth hanging in there through tough times. Your reasons are worth the temporary sacrifices you are making in order to propel you and your family into a better life.

There will be days when you will need to reflect deeply on your reason to keep from throwing in the towel or deciding that none of your instructors know what they are talking about or that you don't have what it takes to learn the content. When you have difficult days, and you will, you need to know that you are NOT alone, you are NOT stupid, and you are NOT the first student to feel badly. You ARE in your right mind, you ARE in the right place - at the right time, and you ARE making a good decision by joining this profession.

I wrote this book as a kind of "tiptionary" or resource manual to inform you of some things that you should take into consideration before beginning nursing school or as you are beginning nursing school. I hope you find it eye-opening and even get a little laugh from my personal anecdotes. I love being a nurse and a nurse educator. I am a huge cheerleader for anyone who wishes to join this profession. This career is very rewarding because it is based on helping people, giving back, and serving.

In fact, you are joining a profession that most people still say is the number one trusted profession on earth. The only time on record where the nursing profession was not number one was 09/11/2001. Can you guess what profession took number one that year? Yes, you guessed it, first responders, first responders who acted selflessly during the terrorist attacks on the United States. A well-deserved honor!

Now, I ask that you sit tight, buckle up, and start slowly by taking a deep breath, preparing your mind for takeoff. Your nursing program will feel like it's going fast, and most programs do, but you will be able to enjoy the ride if you are prepared for where you're going. What I mean by that is take the time to prepare for your lessons by reviewing the night before for the next day, reviewing the week before for the test next week, and reviewing the material you just learned in class that day. Read your assigned readings, view the links and web pages assigned, take notes on the PowerPoints, answer questions in the text, practice NCLEX style questions and take notes on those questions, and come to class prepared to engage in meaningful discussions and activities. Take responsibility and control over your learning. It's impossible for your instructors to teach you everything you will ever need to know for a career in nursing. That is your responsibility. Learning never stops. Nursing school is just the beginning of a lifelong learning path in the field. If you fix your mind and take this approach, then you won't be disappointed. Remember your instructors are human; they don't know everything. But I can promise you this, if you ask and they don't know, they will either find out for you or show you where you can find out.

As you take in this book, I hope you find it resourceful. It is in no way a complete compilation of everything you must remember, but it's a great start as you begin your career. Congratulations, you have made a great investment in your future and the future of your family! Now, have a seat, relax, and enjoy my tips and lessons on nursing school in hopes that they will make your life easier.

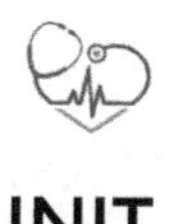

UNIT 1

Your Path

Making the decision to go to nursing school is an important decision. To make the decision, you should take into consideration your background including work experience, lifestyle, desire for employment, time constraints, and current financial status amongst many other individualized criteria.

There are several types of nursing programs, all of which take you down different paths in your career.

Licensed Practical Nurses (LPN)

- diploma program

Registered Nurses (RN)

- associate (ASN or ADN) or bachelor (BSN)

Registered Nurses with Advanced Degrees

- certified registered nurse anesthetists (CRNA)
- certified nurse midwife (CNM)

- nurse practitioner (NP)
- clinical nurse specialist (CNS)

Advanced Degrees for Nurse Educators

- master of science in nursing (MSN)

Doctoral Degrees in Nursing Education or Administration: These are terminal degrees. Terminal means there are no higher degrees than the ones listed below.

- doctor of philosophy (PhD) - An advanced academic research degree in the tradition of science doctorates.
- doctor of nursing practice (DNP) - The doctor of nursing practice degree is an alternative to research focused doctoral programs. It's a clinical practice degree.

Depending on your level of education, you will either take the National Council Licensure Examination - Practical Nurse (NCLEX-PN) or the National Council Licensure Examination - Registered Nurse (NCLEX-RN). Those who obtain a diploma in licensed practical nursing or licensed vocational nursing will take the NCLEX-PN exam, while those who have completed an associate's degree in nursing (ADN) or a bachelor's degree in nursing (BSN) will take the NCLEX-RN exam.

Both exams focus on four specific areas of practice. The areas include: a safe, effective care environment, health promotion and maintenance, preventative healthcare, and psychosocial integrity. The largest element of the NCLEX exam is physiological integrity, which accounts for anywhere from 40-70 percent of all questions. (https://nursejournal.org/articles/6-things-to-know-about-the-nclex-examination)

While LPNs and RNs are both types of nurses who work in various types of medical facilities, RNs require more education and have more responsibility, including advanced job duties, compared to LPNs.

In your job as an LPN, you can work in long-term care facilities, doctors' offices, ambulatory care centers, rehabilitation centers, and dialysis centers to name a few. You may also work in home health, where you can travel to several homes a day or in a private duty setting where you work with one or multiple patients in the same home every day. There are other places open to hiring LPNs. Just do a little bit of research.

RNs are not limited to working in hospital settings. RNs can work in clinics, schools, assisted living facilities, homes, and more.

RNs can also choose specialty areas such as cardiac care, midwifery, family practice, geriatrics, labor and delivery, and emergency nursing. You should know that daily duties can vary greatly depending on the setting.

In an average day, RNs might administer medication, consult with other healthcare providers, monitor patients, do new admission assessments or discharges, educate individuals and families, and be responsible for managing medical records. They must also stay up-to-date with new tools and technology to help provide the best care to patients and families. RNs and LPNs are a valuable part of the healthcare team.

The team can consist of certified nurse aides (CNA), LPNs, RNs, doctors, nutritionists, speech, physical, and occupational therapists, and case managers. Outside of patient care, RNs can eventually attain leadership positions such as nurse managers, nurse educators, and nurse administrators.

All nurses in any setting must possess a strong mix of skills which includes knowledge of technology, communication, emotional and mental intelligence, problem-solving, and critical thinking skills. These are just the tip of the iceberg.

UNIT 2

Your Emotional Health

It's very important that you are mentally and emotionally healthy, so that you are prepared to take care of patients. Not only will you have to deal with your own personal issues, but you will also need to be prepared to hear from your patients and their families as well. If you are solely focused on your own problems, then you won't be able to recognize if your patient is having an emotional or mental issue. This could affect the care they are receiving, or you could possibly miss the fact that their issue requires care.

Do you have the ability to accept constructive criticism? Recognize that constructive criticism is there to help you improve in an area. If you are someone who takes things personally and doesn't see the need for correction, then you probably shouldn't pursue a career in nursing. As a student, you must keep an open mind and be teachable. The healthcare field itself is one that is constantly changing. All of us nurses, doctors, therapists, and the list goes on are learning new things all of the time. Imagine if your doctor decided that she was done learning twenty years ago and never kept a heart that was in pursuit of knowledge. Would you want a doctor using methods that were popular twenty years ago on you now? I think not. So, remain teachable for your entire life.

It's also important that you are able to keep an open mind; see the positive side of people and situations. You must possess character traits like caring, compassion, friendliness, maturity, and respect for coworkers, supervisors, and classmates.

Because your patients are sick, they will have a self-centered viewpoint, but you must make sure that your own life problems are not a problem at work. Your mind must be healthy and focused. Some techniques for maintaining good mental health are to understand yourself, to assess your personality, to examine your personal values, beliefs, prejudices, and to learn to cope effectively with stress.

You must be willing to look at your life and yourself objectively. This is known as self-evaluation. The key to evaluating yourself is a willingness to face and deal with whatever you find, then invest time in personal development (PD). Taking the time for some PD will influence how well you succeed. Because your life has been largely shaped by your experiences, taking the time for PD will help you grow in areas you may not have previously recognized as needing growth. Life has a way of providing opportunities for self-understanding and self-improvement. Without self-understanding you won't be able to understand others and care for them appropriately. Don't get me wrong, no one is perfect, but in order to be a nurse, you must be able to care for others. And at the end of the day, that's why we are all here.

Another method of improving your mental health is to develop good problem-solving skills. Emergencies can arise, taking your attention away from important tasks you have to complete. In these times, good problem-solving skills are of the utmost importance. On the contrary, poor problem-solving skills can lead to a sense of frustration, low self-esteem, and feelings of inadequacy. Not knowing what to do when problems arise can be troubling. When problems occur, they can range from one problem causing many issues to one problem causing one issue or multiple problems causing one or many issues. To help illustrate this, we will use the following example. In the first scenario, a patient has returned to your unit post operation (post-op). You have an order to hang normal saline solution (NSS) for fluid replacement. Instead of the NSS, you mistakenly grab the potassium chloride solution (KCL) and hang it. The fluids run into the patient for one hour before you discover your mistake. Because you hung KCL, which contains potassium, it increased your patient's serum potassium level (amount in their blood). Your patient did not have a need for extra potassium because his levels were fine prior to you administering the fluids. Increased potassium can affect the heart rhythm. Now, the patient needs an EKG, documented vital signs (vs) taken every hour for the next eight hours, labs drawn every six hours for the next twenty-four hours, and a new medication to decrease the amount of potassium in his blood. You will need to place a call to your supervisor, the doctor, and the patient's family to let them know about the mistake. You will also need to inform the patient. You will need to write up an incident report, and you could possibly be suspended for not following facility protocol. As you can see, this problem has spawned into many other consequences and parts. In the second scenario, a patient has returned to your unit post-op. You will need to change the fluids from lactated Ringer's (LR) to normal saline; however, you let an hour go by before discovering that you forgot to do this task. You will need to change the solution and possibly nothing else because the two fluids have many similarities but don't cause a drastic problem with the patient's blood levels or put his life in danger. Nurses get busy and can't immediately do everything on their task list; some tasks can be put off for a little while. As the nurse, you will need to make judgment calls that require good problem-solving skills. When faced with a more immediate emergency, switching the fluids can probably stand to wait a little while and allow you to handle more pressing issues. One way to help solve your problem is to ensure that you lean on your team when needed. You can easily ask your colleague to switch the fluids for you while you attend to other more pressing issues.

As a nurse. you will face your fair share of each of those types of problems. Knowing how to solve them will make you a better, well-adjusted person and will also make you more effective as a nurse.

UNIT 3

Your Support System

I tell all of my students on day *one* that they will need a good support system. I make them take home an oath for their support person(s) to sign and then display it as a mini contract (*See image below*). They usually look at me as if I have two heads, but I am totally serious. You are probably thinking, "Why do they need to sign something?" In nursing school, you will learn a little something called documentation. You can "say" you did something, you can "proclaim" your good intentions, and you can "state" your future actions from now until kingdom come, but if you don't document it, then it wasn't done. You may have given excellent care to your patients all day long, and they may give you rave reviews, but if you didn't document it, then you didn't do it.

Take this approach when asking someone to be a support system for you. It can serve as a visual reminder for them and for you. You don't have to use my exact words but create something similar if it makes you feel better. Think of it like a contract. Contracts are admissible in court. Communicate the contract to your support system in that manner, showing that you are serious because school is serious. No, you wouldn't take them to court over being unavailable on any given day with no time to help you, but you do expect them to take this seriously and help you when they can. You can work out the specific terms with the person/people you choose when the time comes.

It's important that before embarking on a huge undertaking like school, you have a solid support system in place. Your support system can be one person or many people. They should be people who can agree to help you through school by taking care of children, giving you rides when your car breaks down, and providing a shoulder to cry on when you want to pull your hair out, or even be a listening ear when you want to go upside your classmates head but can't.

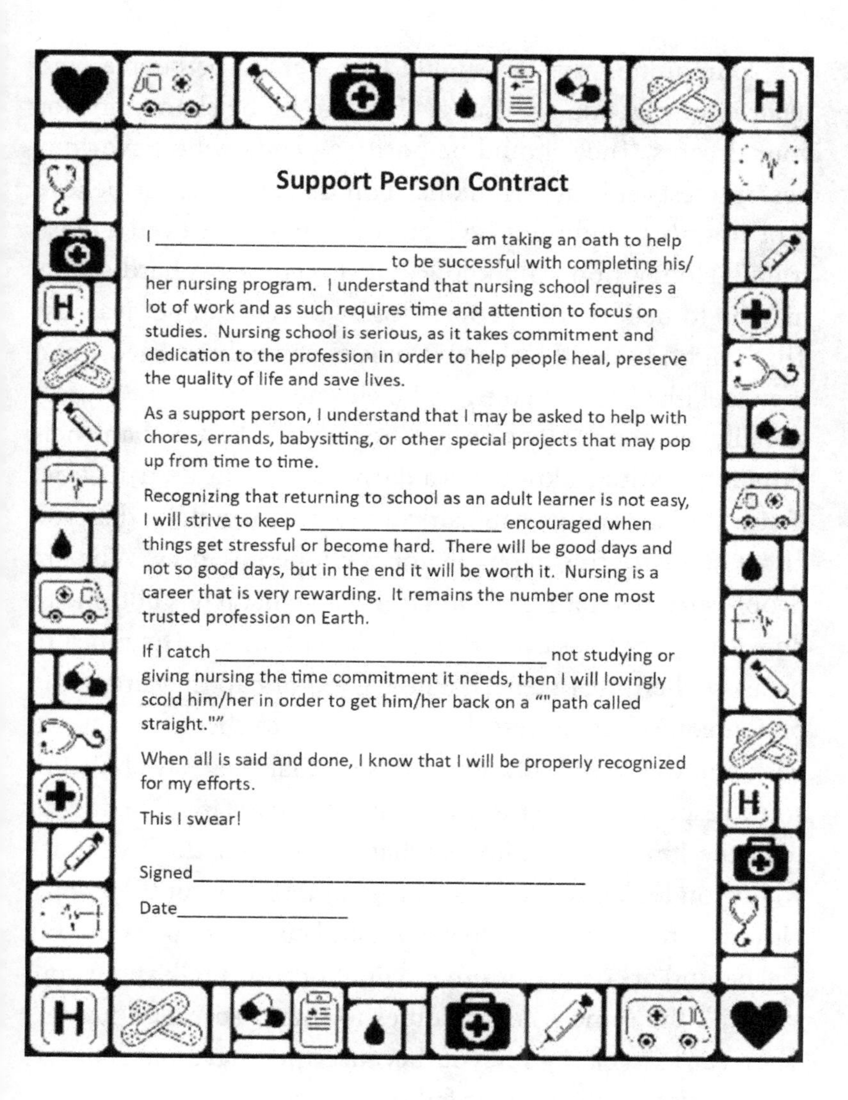

Support Person Contract

I ______________________________ am taking an oath to help ________________________ to be successful with completing his/her nursing program. I understand that nursing school requires a lot of work and as such requires time and attention to focus on studies. Nursing school is serious, as it takes commitment and dedication to the profession in order to help people heal, preserve the quality of life and save lives.

As a support person, I understand that I may be asked to help with chores, errands, babysitting, or other special projects that may pop up from time to time.

Recognizing that returning to school as an adult learner is not easy, I will strive to keep ____________________ encouraged when things get stressful or become hard. There will be good days and not so good days, but in the end it will be worth it. Nursing is a career that is very rewarding. It remains the number one most trusted profession on Earth.

If I catch ________________________________ not studying or giving nursing the time commitment it needs, then I will lovingly scold him/her in order to get him/her back on a ""path called straight.""

When all is said and done, I know that I will be properly recognized for my efforts.

This I swear!

Signed______________________________________

Date________________

Your support system should be a person or people who believe in what you are doing. They should be champions for your dreams. They should be positive people who have your best interests at heart. Think hard on this one because believe it or not, this might not be a family member or even a close friend. Honey, don't you know that sometimes as hard as this may be to believe, the people closest to you can get jealous? That's right! I said it! Jealous! People become threatened when they feel like you are going to be elevated personally, professionally, or financially to a position that is better than their situation. I know, I know, it's a darn shame, but it's true. I bet if you think about it, you can come up with a story that you know of where this happened or is happening now. Why are people such haters? I'll tell you right now that it has nothing to do with you but has everything to do with them. They start to measure their life in terms of how good or bad they are doing by someone else's success. In their minds, to cheer for you and wish you well is literally an admission that they have failed in some respect. Another term for that behavior is, "Keeping up with the Joneses." You know what that means, don't you? It's when you look outside, and your neighbor has cut their yard. Now, you feel compelled to get out and cut yours, so you don't feel behind or so that the other neighbors don't talk about you. Well, it's the same when it comes to these "so-called haters." They can't be happy for you because they have internalized your success to mean their failure. Crazy, right?

A word of caution: choose your support system wisely! Ask yourself the following question. "Is he or she able to agree with and adhere to the statements in the Support System Agreement above?" It's important that a copy of this agreement is distributed to everyone you've chosen. This way they can remember what they agreed to. Ask them to keep it in a place that is readily available. There may be times when they need to reflect back on what they've agreed to. Everyone needs a little reminder sometimes just in case they start to fake the funk or suddenly come down with a case of amnesia...yeah right!

Some criteria to consider when choosing a good support system are listed next. It's important that you first make a list of every possible person who you can consider. After you make your list, sift through it using my criteria and suggestions to see who you are left with.

Once you have narrowed down your choices to one person or a handful of people, I suggest you hold a small soiree (that's just a fancy word for a small gathering or get together) to announce that you've decided to go to nursing school, but try to bring a little bit of drama into your announcement. Have some light refreshments for the people and maybe a little gift. It can even be from the dollar store. Hey, it's not cheap. It's called being frugal or just plain trying not to overdo it. You know the saying, "It's the thought that counts."

Try to make this event a big deal. Your people will appreciate you and are much more likely to say yes. Of course, you don't have to do it like this but think of a fun way to announce your "big news." Think about it, people have come up with all sorts of creative ways to announce the gender of their unborn children. Why not be equally creative in announcing your decision to enter nursing school? It *is* something you are trying to birth. It will be a new life for you and your family! If all else fails, making a phone call is nice too. Don't forget the thank you card! I am *still* a fan of old-fashioned thank you cards. I keep stocked up on them. There is something to be said for the fact that someone sits down and takes the time to handwrite or at least sign a generic card. If you don't have the means to include a small gift, then place an IOU inside. Your support system will appreciate it. Just don't give a "dry" card. What's a "dry" card, you ask? A dry card is one where there is *nothing* inside. (My daughter taught me this. Thanks, Tay.) We have all gotten them for our birthdays. You open the card because that's all the person gave you, and when you open it, it's just the card. Now, be honest. When you opened the card, you were so disappointed that it was empty, that you didn't even want to read it. We can blame that on our childhood. We got used to opening birthday cards that at least had a few dollars in it! I don't care if it's an IOU for a cup of coffee. Please put something in the dang-blang card. Okay, back to business.

- First and foremost, your support system must be **available.** Is it someone who has the time in their life to help you on short notice? For example, if your child's daycare closes suddenly on a morning you have to be in class, will your support system be able to spring into action to make sure you won't have to miss school?

- Your support system must be **willing**. Will your support system take the initiative to reach out to you if they notice you need the help? Sometimes we don't notice those times when we should reach out. Your support system should be in tune to your behaviors. The bottom line is to take the help when it is offered. You won't prove a thing by failing your test because you were too proud to ask for help with the kids to allow yourself two hours of solitude for studying.
- Your support system should have a **good attitude** about life in general. People with positive outlooks on life will generally feel positive about you. You don't want someone who is mean and cantankerous being your support system. Just no!
- Your support system must be **trustworthy.** Can you trust them with your most precious investment...your children? If you don't have children, can you trust them with your feelings? Will they keep your trust if you confide in them?
- That brings me to a **confidant.** Your support system must also be a confidant. A confidant is a person you can share a secret or a personal matter with. They should be someone who can be trusted not to repeat the private matters of your heart. The opposite of a confidant is someone who

will share your business up and down the street. You don't want or need that. You ain't tryna, that's right, I said tryna (country slang for trying to) catch a case when you're trying to pull up to the next level of greatness in your life. Ain't nobody got time for that!

- Your support system must be an **encourager.** Is your support system a natural caretaker? Do they usually have words of encouragement for you or others in their orbit? Shoot, everybody ought to keep a couple of encouraging statements in their back pocket just in case they need to use them from time to time.

- Your support system must be **strong**. More likely than not, your support system will have a family of their own. Will they be able to take on the extra responsibility if you need them? Can they manage their own kids and yours too? Or are they someone who is a pushover or easily persuaded? Will the kids run all over them? Or do they know when to put their foot down?

- Your support system must be a **defender.** Is your support system someone who usually sticks up for people or good causes in general? This will give you an idea of whether they will defend you to jealous family members, friends, your own children, and even --get this one...yourself. There *may* be days when you feel so overwhelmed that you think about quitting. Nursing school is work, hard work! Your support system must be a defender of good ideas. Your decision to go to nursing school is a good idea! Remember that when times get tough.

- Finally, your support system must be **empowered**! They must be empowered by you to make decisions. Some of these decisions could be concerning your children in cases of emergency. Some of these decisions may be decisions on your behalf if you are not able to be present in some respect. They must be empowered to speak on your behalf.

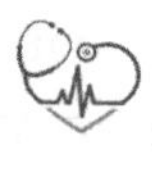

UNIT 4

Your Resources

Now, let's discuss your resources. It's important to take inventory of what resources you have available that will allow your time in nursing school to flow more effectively. Your resources are anything that you can use to make life easier while you are in school. Everyone's list may be a little different. Your support system is one resource, and as discussed previously, your support system is probably your most valuable resource.

Another less-glamorous resource is a fully stocked pantry. This is a tactic you may want to use. Go shopping for all of your dry groceries and non-perishable items ahead of time. Literally take a couple of months to stock your pantry with an overflow supply of those essential goods while you are still working full-time. That way, if you are not able to continue with full-time employment once you're in school, then half of your battle will be done. I say half because you will still need to shop for perishable items such as produce, meat, frozen foods, and dairy. At least your future grocery trips will be shorter, allowing more time in your schedule to study, run other errands, or to spend time with your family.

Take an inventory of where you have money saved or invested. Do you have a savings account or other type of account you can borrow against, or maybe you have an investment that's nearing maturity that you can access to obtain cash? View it as an investment in your future by supplying your immediate needs now. That's literally what savings should do. Savings should provide a source of income for you in times of need. Consider using some of your savings to help meet your basic needs while in school, that way, you don't have to work as much and therefore will have more time for your studies. You must think about the things in your life that will save you time, decrease expenses, or increase income.

Another resource is a side hustle. If you don't have one, then think about getting one. An appropriate side hustle for a nursing student is one that does not require you to leave your house to make money. This could be Paparazzi Jewelry, Thirty-One, Total Life Changes (TLC), or creating a blog, YouTube channel, or a podcast. These are just a few ideas that come to mind. If you have a cell phone, then you can have a business. By the way, visit my side hustle page at https://retail.totallifechanges.com/NurseTalonda for the latest, greatest health and wellness products. If you need to lose a few pounds, then we have the products for you. If you want an easy business you can do from the comfort of your own home, contact me via my website https://riscqhealthcare.com and fill out the inquiry form. Someone from my team will get back to you within forty-eight hours. Shameless plug over. You see side hustles are not only for nursing students, but nursing instructors also have side hustles and other businesses. Back to the subject at hand, any of these businesses are something you can do while on a break from studying. Devoting two to three hours on a Saturday and Sunday toward your side hustle in order to generate income is just enough to keep money flowing through your pockets. A side hustle can prevent you from having to work 12-hour shifts that take you away from your family and away from your studies.

You could also clean out your closets, kids' closets, husband's closet, and basement, looking for hidden gems that can be sold on eBay, social media yard sale sites, or in an actual yard sale. I know that some of you are thinking that you don't have anything to sell. Let me enlighten you, people will buy anything! That "thing" you own, sitting in the corner and collecting dust, well clean it off, and then sell it. It might be that weird item that someone is looking for. You have no clue how many hidden gems are in your possession if you would just take the time to look. I'm sure you are all familiar with the saying, "One man's trash is another man's treasure." Well, there you go. Clean up and clear out; you could be sitting on a few hundred dollars. Will the money meet every need for the entire time you are in nursing school? Probably not, but it could put food on your table and gas in your car for a few weeks. So, make that money honey!

A side hustle can also allow you time to study while on breaks. The key is to be able to care for your family's needs, while focusing on your studies. I once had a student become very upset about my speech to her class. In my speech, I told the students that it would be difficult to successfully complete the program while working full-time. Is it possible to be successful in the program while working full time? Yes, but it's more difficult because you are literally splitting your time. The student ended up proving me right because she failed level one of the program. Of course, I wasn't happy to hear this, but it is a good example for you to hear, helping you recognize that your studies are extremely important while in school.

Your studying and ability to get good grades are directly related to the kind of care you will give as a nurse; the kind of care you give can be the difference between life and death. Take your studies seriously. You are in school to become a nurse *not* an aide. If you want to elevate, then you must be willing to make the hard decisions. You must be willing to live on *less* now in order to have *more* later. Please understand that I am not putting down or belittling the job of a nurse's aide. I am a champion of nurse's aides. I recognize that I couldn't do my job effectively without good aides by my side. But *you* made the decision to go to nursing school for a reason. Remember that reason. Remember that you must devote a lot of time to your dream to help it come true.

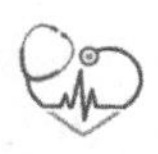

UNIT 5

Your Thoughts

Don't let your thoughts ruin your chances of success. It's important to think positive. Cut out the stinkin' thinkin'. Shout out to Steve Urkel (Jalil White), the quirky star of *Family Matters*, a TV show from the 90s. Anyway, your thoughts can and will literally materialize into the things you focus your attention on. I read that in the book, *Think and Grow Rich* by Napoleon Hill, and it made sense to me. Everything that was created began with a thought or an idea. Ideas begin in your mind. Once you have the idea or thought, then you begin to work on creating the thing. Things are tangible. In nursing school, if you focus or imagine (thought) getting good grades (things), then it most certainly can happen. Get ahold of your thoughts now. Enter nursing school with the right attitude and mindset. You must first believe that you can do this because you can do anything you put your mind to. I tell my girls, Tayah and Rena, this all of the time as I'm sure many of you tell your kids.

I remember when I decided to go back to school for my RN, I was genuinely freaking out. I was going to be in school four days a week and then fit all of my forty hours of work in spread over three days and one evening. Yes, I was nuts, but it worked for me. I was so grateful to the facility I worked in; they were flexible and allowed me to do it. I remember being at work one day, feeling down about what I was about to embark on. I knew that not only would it be challenging, but I would also have limited time for my family. But at the same time, I knew that this move would help elevate my family to a better position financially. I specifically remember feeling really down one night at work. A nurse I worked with told me that *I can do anything temporarily*. I took that to heart. In fact, that statement got me through some very tough days. It was such a true declaration, and it was from the heart.

Make sure to fill your mind with positive thoughts. Do you use affirmations? If you don't, you should. Google "positive affirmations," and then post your affirmations everywhere. Post them on your bathroom mirror, your refrigerator, in your car, and on your notebooks. This will help set your mind straight when you start thinking negatively. Side note (courtesy of my friend Dina): When you tell someone they did a good job, you say, "Great job!" When someone does something bad, you say, "What in the world were you thinking? How could you have been so careless? You need to do better next time!" Moral: Two words when someone does good, 80,000 words when they don't. Which do you think they'll remember? It is essential that we work to counteract that negative force. Thinking positive is work! Work requires action. If you want better, then you have to do better. Before you can do, you must think. Now, do you see that everything starts in the mind? We can literally do nothing unless our mind tells us to. So, pay your mind some respect by giving it something positive to think about.

Another method I want you to use is listening to motivational speakers on YouTube. Believe me, there are plenty. Start by picking just two and see if you vibe with their story. Listen every day, every chance you get. Don't only gravitate to the same sex motivational speakers. I have gotten a lot out of male motivational speakers. I listen to different motivational speakers for different areas in my life. They are almost like counselors but very cheap. I like cheap!

If you wake up and immediately get on social media, then you will allow the stories to control your emotions. YOU need to be in control of your emotions instead of being sucked in by who did or did not "like" your latest selfie or latest post. You will soon find yourself mindlessly scrolling through posts, liking and commenting, and when you finally look up, three hours will have gone by. And don't get me started on the time you can waste on TikTok!

Also, don't even think about turning on the TV to watch the news. We all know that the news will depress us. If not depress us, it can certainly make us angry. Especially with what's been happening lately, way too much "fake news" especially from the creator of that saying! Do yourself a favor; stay off of social media and keep the TV off! Instead, *do* take the time to focus your thoughts on what you want to accomplish for the day.

Say your positive affirmations when you get up in the morning and before you go to bed at night. It's important to establish a routine and good habits while in school. When you wake up in the morning, don't immediately go check your social media pages. Yes pages! Take this time in the morning for yourself. You need time to reflect and plan your day. Create this habit, and it will become a routine. A routine is second nature. You don't have to think about it. It's as if your brain is on autopilot.

First thing in the morning, take the time to pray and thank God for waking you up to see another day. Then meditate on His word, allowing it to sink in. It doesn't have to be a lot, simply start with one sentence from the Bible. Take the time and let it sink into your soul. Next, on a piece of paper or in your phone's notes app, jot down five goals you want to accomplish for the day. Make the goals extra-realistic to ensure you accomplish all of them. Allowing yourself that amazing sense of daily accomplishment is extremely important. You'll be able to feel that same sense of achievement when you make those small accomplishments in school. Start these little tasks now. Before starting school, make it a habit!

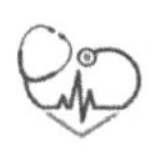

UNIT 6

Your Study Place – Study Space

I had a student who couldn't find a quiet place to study, so I suggested she study in her car. In her car, she could be away from the hustle and bustle of her house. She made it her permanent study space, which worked out perfectly for her. She thanked me when she found that her grades were rising due to the time she was devoting to her studies after she found the solace she needed. You see, all I did was suggest that she think outside of the box a bit. I told her that her house might not be the best place to focus on her studies. If any of you are like me, then you will find any reason to procrastinate. Suddenly the lamps need dusting, the kitchen cabinets need to be organized, and you have to run to the store to rent the carpet shampooer because your carpets haven't been cleaned in six months. Do yourself a favor and get away from your house to study. If none of the things I mentioned are a concern or worry for you, then imagine your kids demanding all of your time. Some of you may have kids that are old enough to understand not to bother you during study time, but if you have toddlers, you can forget it.

You will need a quiet place for studying. That might be your room, a corner in your house, or even the bathroom. Hey, it can be just about anywhere that is away from the hustle and bustle of the house. Nursing school is different, and it demands to be treated as such. You will have plenty of material to study and assignments to complete, so it's a good idea to carve out that special place for yourself, where you can focus. You must give school the time it needs by devoting a lot of time to your studies. There is no way around it. If you don't pass your tests, you will fail out. And honestly, that's probably a good thing; nobody wants a nurse that doesn't know what they are doing.

When you find or claim this study space in your home, it's important that the rest of the people in your house be aware that when you are studying, you are off limits. Basically, they should pretend you're not home. I used to tell my kids, "If it ain't broken, bleeding, or on fire, don't bother me." I was totally serious. If you can't find that quiet space in your home, then consider the library, a family member's home, or staying after school to utilize the school's library.

While you're in school, it's expected that you will spend a minimum of two to three hours per day on your studies, and that's during the week. On the weekends, be sure to devote at least five to six hours a day. Break it up something like this: Saturday, 10 a.m.-12 p.m., 2 p.m.- 4 p.m., and then 8 p.m.-10 p.m. This schedule affords you plenty of time to wake up, make breakfast for your family, eat lunch, and have dinner and quiet time with your family before putting the kids to bed. It also allows you to end your studies with enough time to get a good night's sleep. Sunday, get right back at it: 7 a.m.-9 a.m., leaving time to attend church service, then 2 p.m.-4 p.m., and then 8 p.m.-10 p.m. If you work on the weekends for example, dayshift eight hours, then study from 5 p.m.-7 p.m. and then pick it up again 9 p.m.-11 p.m. If you don't have to be in until the evening shift, then study from 8 a.m.-10 a.m., and then 12 p.m.-2 p.m. If you work a twelve-hour day shift on the weekend, study from 9 p.m.-11 p.m. and hopefully you take advantage of your breaks and lunch/dinner to pull out some note cards to get a little more studying time in. If you work a twelve-hour night shift, hopefully, you utilize the downtime overnight, but also wake up by 3 or 4 p.m. That way you can have dinner with your family, then study from 4 p.m.-6 p.m. or at least the bare minimum of one hour. Do you see how easy it is to get study time in on the weekends? Take advantage of any time you can get and put some study time in!

Here is another tip: Take your notes everywhere you go. When I was in school, I took my notes everywhere. I took them to the grocery store, to dinner with my family, and even over to my family's house for Thanksgiving. I never wanted to miss an opportunity where there was time on my hands, and I didn't have my notes to review. I used note cards. They were small enough to fit in my pocket. I could pull them out quickly and discreetly glance at them while waiting for food in restaurants, sitting at a traffic light, or socializing on holidays. I know it seems extreme, but it's really not. When you're in school, you have to maximize every opportunity to gain knowledge. On the rare occasion when I did forget to bring my notes when I went out, I felt upset. I felt like something was missing and that I was wasting time.

If this all sounds like overkill to you, it is! Remember that school is a sacrifice, and it's only temporary, and you can do anything temporarily.

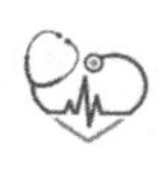

UNIT 7

Nursing School Is Different from High School

I was a good student in high school. I got straight As and graduated with honors. When entering nursing school, I wasn't prepared for how rigorous the work would be. This is not to scare you. Hopefully, you don't scare that easily. This is to help put your mind in a different mindset, ensuring you are prepared to think of nursing school as something different, a different type of schooling that will stretch you, bend you, twist you, but won't break you. As long as you don't let it. Keep in mind that there have been many a student that wanted to break but didn't. And you won't break either! I mean you signed up for a reason. That reason got you to this point, and you *need* to remember that reason when times get hard, and you feel like you want to break or give up.

I'm not going to sugarcoat anything. Nursing school can be hard. But to quote one of my favorite motivational speakers, Les Brown, "If it's hard, then do it hard!" Thank you, Mr. Brown, because whenever I get ready to complain about something feeling insurmountable, I think of your words. You can't let hard be a reason why you quit or give up. Anything worth having is worth fighting for. You've all heard that expression before. Why do we think that life is supposed to be easy? Why do we assume that good things are supposed to just fall into our laps? Who told you that you wouldn't need to have to push through, fight, or struggle to help your dreams come true? Most students who enter nursing school usually say that it's been their dream to become a nurse. Every student has their own reason why becoming a nurse is their dream. Each reason is unique and holds a special meaning to the individual. I always stress to my students that they should remember their reason when tough times come because they *will* come. It's going to be up to you to dig deep and keep that reason "top of mind" to help push you past any negative feelings.

The ability to push past negative feelings is part of what distinguishes an adult learner from a high school student. Adults realize that many times it's do or die! They don't have mommy or daddy to fall back on financially or even sometimes emotionally. Instead, it's the adult looking their child in the face, needing to make it happen, knowing that in a short while if they don't give up, a better life is coming.

High School	Nursing School
Teen lives at home with parents	Adult often lives on own (family, single)
Content only/Memorization	Content/Hands on Application
Studies to get by	Studies to know it (lives depend on it)
May study 1 hour/night	Must study a minimum of 2-3 hours/night
Can go out with friends on the weekends	Probably will be studying on the weekends
Can get housework/ chores done	Will not always get housework/chores done
May have a car/bus available to get to school	Must have own reliable transportation for school and clinical
Can complete work without support	Should have a support system
May not be organized but can be successful	Should be organized for success
Attendance and punctuality important but not a reason for expulsion	Attendance and punctuality important or can be dismissed from the program

UNIT 8

Diversity and Connection

Nursing school brings people together from all different walks of life. I was not prepared to meet so many people who didn't hold my same values and beliefs. No one is right or wrong; we're just different. I learned that it was okay to have a variety of different personalities and attitudes in one class. It actually contributed to making me a more well-rounded thinker. I'm not saying that it was always rainbows and unicorns in the class, but overall, we all learned to deal with each other's idiosyncrasies and work it out. I saw a different scene play out in some cohorts that started after me. A cohort is simply a group of students that go through the program together from start to finish. I still see it now as an instructor, and it's really unfortunate because your ability to get along with or tolerate different people's personalities is directly related to your level of maturity. Believe it or not, we have to bring in speakers on the subject of incivility from time to time. There have also been some cohorts that get along really well. It's nice as an instructor to see students pulling together to help one another. Then there are others who can't wait to graduate, so they don't have to see each other ever again. I think it's sad because forming comraderies while you progress through the program is important. It's no good to be on an island by yourself. It's nice to have friendships. It'll make your journey a little easier.

When you start working in the field of nursing, you will need to get along with your colleagues, ensuring that continuity of care stays intact. You don't have to be best friends with the people you work with, but there should be an atmosphere of cooperation where the patients can benefit. It will make your patients feel better knowing that their nurse has a tolerance for different people and differing viewpoints. Now, replace the word colleagues with your classmates. Mastering skills of tolerance for people with different viewpoints begins in the classroom. People *will* get on your nerves. Some days you will feel like you have one nerve left and someone who is annoying you will be on it. It's on those days that you must resist the urge to do or say things that are not productive or conducive to your own learning or others'. And of course, remember *why* you chose to go to nursing school.

Sometimes, we can get locked in our own little brains and tend to believe that our way is *the* way. My early years in nursing school taught me that just because I *think* it's right does not *make* it right. I'm not speaking about any particular incident; I'm referring to my way of thinking. If you know me, you will know that this is a very hard thing for me to admit. Hey, it's in my DNA! Give me forty-five more years; I'm working on it.

To be in a profession like healthcare, you must get used to meeting and interacting with many different people. You should also have compassion for people. You must develop a love for different ideas and points of view. It will actually help you with your—get ready for this word—you will hear this many times during your educational journey—you will be begging your teachers to define it so that you can understand it better—you will need to draw on ideas and solutions you didn't even know were in your brain—it will actually help you with your—drum roll please—I mentioned it in the very first unit of this book—drum roll please . . . CRITICAL THINKING! That's right people. When you consider other people's point of view, you are better equipped to figure things out, put the pieces of the puzzle together, draw on your own prior experiences and current learning, and reason and talk through situations in an effort to solve problems. Yes, that's critical thinking! To learn more about critical thinking, you can visit this link https://bit.ly/2YQg0L2

UNIT 9

Classroom Dynamics

You've made it to your first day of school. You're excited because you've been looking forward to starting school. This is a career change for you. Maybe you've been a stay-at-home mother for years, and now that the kids are in school full-time, you're going to do something for you. Or maybe you are a private contractor, and because business has been slow, your wife has convinced you to go to nursing school. No matter which path led you here, you are here! You are going to take the leap and pursue a career that has the potential to propel your life in a totally new direction.

You have been marking the days off the calendar for the past three months. You've passed your entrance test for acceptance into your chosen program and gotten all of your health records up to date. You've visited your doctor to get your titers, seeing that it's been umpteen years since you had shots, and you can't find your old dusty records that are probably buried in your stacks of papers because you are a hoarder at heart. (See the following link that will explain all about a TI-

TER in a very simple and easy way. https://medlineplus.gov/ency/article/003333.htm) You've taken your drug test, completed CPR training, and obtained your tuberculin skin test. You've spent hours in the school supplies aisle at your favorite superstore, making sure you have every color highlighter and those cool gel pens because you like the way they glide across the paper. You have notebooks, planners, book covers, and other supplies galore. You've even pulled out your carry-on luggage to lug home all of the books you will have just like the director of the program told you to bring on your first day!

It's finally here, the night before the first day of school. You feel excited and nervous all rolled up into one. You've made your family a great dinner, and everyone has gone to bed on time for once. You want to get a good night's sleep, so that you are bright-eyed and bushy-tailed in the morning, ready to tackle this new chapter of your life. Your husband has even taken the initiative, for once, to fill up your gas tank, ensuring you don't have to make any unnecessary stops on your way to school in the morning. You fall asleep with a smile on your face.

The next morning you arise before your alarm is set to go off at 6 a.m. You get the children's breakfast and get them out the door for school. As the sun begins to come up over the horizon and peak through your kitchen window, you sip freshly brewed coffee from your favorite coffee mug and take a few moments to reflect on what this new beginning means to you and the future of your family. You get the "warm and fuzzies." Thanks, Yolonda; I had to shout out my sis for that term. Anyway, you finish your coffee, jump in the shower, get dressed, and kiss your husband goodbye because he has the luxury of not rising until an hour after you, and you head out the door. School starts at 8 a.m. You get there at 7:30 a.m. to secure a good parking space. You enter the building at 7:45 a.m., heading to your class. There are fifteen other students who had the same idea as you, and you all enter the classroom at the same time and take seats. Some sit in the front, some sit in the back, but you prefer the middle. People make small talk, including you. You feel really good about the start of your day. Two nursing instructors and the director enter the room for introductions and orientation. The day is pretty easy, consisting of a few icebreaker games, an overview of your classes, individual introductions on why you decided to come to nursing school, then it's lunch time, and the day is over. You pack your stack of books in your rolling carry-on and head out of the building for home.

The next day reality sets in as you begin to learn nursing content. You discover that there is a lot of information to learn and that nursing school sounds like it will be a challenge. You get through the day with a ton of note-taking, some minor computer challenges, and you've even made a couple of friends. You are very optimistic and continue to feel happy about the changes you are making in your life, knowing that nursing school holds the key to unlock a future that is bright, a future that is full, and a future that is lucrative. You have made a great decision for your family.

Days go by and some of your classmates seem needier than others. Their constant interruption of the teacher is annoying because you are a good listener, and you'd like to go through the content at an even pace. They seem to ask a lot of questions. The questions they are asking are trivial and commonsense type questions. Most of the time, you think to yourself if they would just hold their questions a little while, they would discover that the teacher would address that very topic as part of her presentation. This is really beginning to get under your skin as it becomes a constant distraction on a daily basis.

Fast forward a couple of months, and you have definitely decided who you can't tolerate, who you don't care for, and who you thoroughly enjoy in the class. Some people ask a lot of questions, some people seem to have bad attitudes, some people have formed cliques, some people are disrespectful to the teacher, and some talk loudly while you are trying to study during self-directed time. You really love the content you are learning and want to become a nurse because it's your passion. However, some of your classmates are so intolerable that there are days you don't want to go to school, instead wishing you could just stay home and take notes from your PowerPoint slides and textbook. If it continues like this, you are not sure how much longer you will be able to stand being in school. Suddenly, the person who was so excited about this new chapter in her life is now questioning the very decision to go to school all because you decide that you don't like most of your classmates.

What you must get and get now is...what you must understand and know is... people will annoy you! It's a fact of life. Expect people to be people. What I mean is, expect that they will pluck your *last* nerve. Expect that some people are immature, ignorant, rude, needy, have a high-school mentality, don't know any better, form cliques, talk about people, disrupt the class, and have no home-training. Be aware of those behaviors, and you won't be caught off guard and eventually disappointed.

Remember there is a flip side to the annoying, rude, disrespectful, and immature students. On the flip side are the good students. These are your people, the group that you vibe with. These students are helpful and encouraging to others. These students spend time studying and offering and giving good feedback to their classmates and instructors. These students form study groups and invite everyone or create study materials and share it with the class. These students want to see everyone succeed because they view the class as a team. These students are not perfect but strive to do their best. This group came to school for the right reasons and have learned how to coexist with people they don't necessarily understand or agree with. That's what it's like to work with people in general. I can promise you that you won't like everyone you work with, but you will learn how to coexist for the benefit of the patients you have to care for.

So, when people act in ways that are not beneficial or conducive to a healthy learning environment, try to come up with ways you can all coexist for the benefit of learning. I can hear the chorus of "Thank yous" in my head, so I'll just say, "You're welcome."

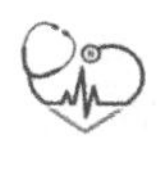

UNIT 10

The Be-Attitudes of Nursing

"Your attitude not your aptitude, will determine your altitude." This quote comes from the great motivational speaker and author, Zig Ziglar. Mr. Ziglar is absolutely right. In order to accomplish anything, you must first have the right attitude. What attitude are you displaying daily, weekly, monthly, yearly? Is it a "can-do" attitude or a "can't-do" attitude? Because no matter which it is, you are right. If you believe you can, then you will begin to manifest those qualities that help you succeed. If you believe you can't, then you will begin to manifest those qualities that will ensure that you won't succeed. It's called the Law of Attraction. See the link below to learn more about manifesting through the Law of Attraction. www.thelawofattraction.com/manifest-something-want-24hrs-less/

The brain is a very powerful organ. It has to be because it's the boss of the entire body. Yes, that's right. You can influence your success by how you think about it.

Do you have the right attitude for success, or have you already defeated yourself before you even get started? Some people are so prone to negative thinking that they will simply sabotage themselves before they get started. Self-sabotage is real. It's literally a fear of success. Whenever something good happens or can begin to happen, you or sometimes the people close to you will do something to sabotage it. For instance, one year for lent, I had my husband and teenage daughters on board to give up sugar for forty days. We were well on our way and succeeding. We lost weight and felt good about ourselves, then entered my MOTHER. She questioned why we would be doing such a "crazy" thing. She even asked me why I was depriving my kids. She told them how they should be able to have a sweet treat every now and then. She went so far as to drop off cookies and ice cream to my house for the kids. What did this do? Well, it convinced my kids that what they were doing was silly because after all, they are kids and they do deserve a sweet treat every now and then. Well, that was it. My children had been sabotaged and the thirty straight days of progress was ruined. Needless to say, I was angry. I wondered why she would sabotage our progress, especially after I explained why we were doing it. I then remembered that she was trying to lose weight herself. You see some people will sabotage you if they are jealous. Either knowingly or unknowingly, their "good" intentions are still sabotage. Bottom line is beware when you are sabotaging yourself or when others are doing it to you.

Some of you may have some people in your lives that you need to give the boot, kiss goodbye, say sayonara, au revoir, arrivederci, see ya later, don't let the door knob hit ya where the dog shoulda bit ya! Shout out to Pam (Tichina Arnold) from *Martin*, the best TV show of the 90s. Hey, it's my book, my opinion. You get the point. If the people in your life are not encouraging, loving, and helpful, then they are not healthy to have around for the sake of your attitude. Sadly, sometimes that includes family. Remember, not everyone in your life will be happy that you're in nursing school. That old saying "like crabs in a bucket" may come into play. As soon as one tries to climb to the top of the bucket, the others will pull him back down. It's a way of thinking best described by the phrase "If I can't have it, neither can you." The metaphor is derived from a pattern of behavior noted in crabs when they are trapped in a bucket. Here's another, "Misery loves company." Be wary of people who don't want to see you succeed. Most of the time, it's because of their own fear that when you become successful, you will leave them or that you will change. And the truth is, you should change. You are on to something bigger and better. It's time to leave the childish things behind. Some of you have some strongholds and barriers in your life based on the way you grew up that will hinder you from changing to a more positive mindset or attitude. It may be the culture of your very neighborhood. Or get this one, it may be the culture of your very family. It's ingrained in you. I'm here to tell you that you must fight through that stronghold in order to have better and become better, for yourself and for your family.

In order to be successful in any nursing program, you must *be* many things. I have compiled a list of what I know is important. This list is in no way exhaustive. I call it the Be-attitudes of Nursing, a nod to the book of Matthew, Chapter 5 in the Bible.

You should write a couple of your own directly in this book. I'll leave three lines for you…

- Blessed are the courteous, for others will be courteous to you.
- Blessed are the thoughtful, for it will translate well when taking care of your patients.
- Blessed are those who value studying, for you'll do well on many tests.
- Blessed are those who don't gossip about fellow students, for others will learn to trust you.
- Blessed are those who are helpful to classmates, for there will be a day when you need help.
- Blessed are those who show up on time, for yours is a great recommendation from the faculty.
- Blessed are those who participate in class, for you will get out what you put in.
- Blessed are those who ask for help, for you will receive it.
- Blessed are those who make an effort, for you shall see that effort pay off.
- Blessed are those who respect their faculty, for you shall be shown respect.
- Blessed are the professional, for it will take you far in this career, opening many doors for you.
- Blessed are ______________________________

- Blessed are ______________________________
- Blessed are ______________________________

I think out of everything we will discuss in this book, if you remember these Be-attitudes of Nursing School, you will do well.

UNIT 11

Handling Your Stress

Stress can be difficult to understand and sometimes difficult to identify. It can cause a lot of emotional chaos and wreak havoc on your body, sometimes having detrimental consequences. Strangely enough, we are not always aware that we are under stress. There are, however, habits, attitudes, and signs that we do have stress, but they can be hard to recognize because we are so familiar with stress. Some of us on a daily basis.

Kurzen, in the 8th edition of Practical/Vocational Nursing, compiled a chart of criteria to help you figure out your stress level. How high is your stress level? Fill in the chart, and then tally your score.

Do you frequently:	**Yes**	**No**
Neglect your diet?		
Try to do everything yourself?		
Blow up easily?		
Seek unrealistic goals?		

Do you frequently:	**Yes**	**No**
Fail to see the humor in situations others find funny?		
Act rude?		
Make a "big deal" of everything?		
Look to other people to make things happen?		
Complain that you are disorganized?		
Avoid people whose ideas are different from your own?		
Keep everything inside?		
Neglect exercise?		
Have few supportive relationships?		
Use sleeping pills and tranquilizers without a doctor's approval?		
Get too little rest?		
Get angry when you are kept waiting?		
Ignore stress symptoms?		
Put things off until later?		
Think there is only one right way to do something?		
Fail to build relaxation time into your day?		
Gossip?		
Race through the day?		

Do you frequently:	Yes	No
Spend a lot of time complaining about the past?		
Fail to get a break from noise and crowds?		
Total your score (1 for each Yes: 0 for each No)		

(Kurzen, 2017)

SCORING

1-6: There are few hassles in your life. Make sure that you are not trying so hard to avoid problems that you shy away from challenges.

7-13: You've got your life in fairly good control. Work on the choices and habits that could still be causing you some unnecessary stress in your life.

14-20: You're approaching the danger zone. You may well be suffering stress-related symptoms, and your relationships could be strained. Think carefully about choices you have made and take relaxation breaks every day.

More than 20 points: Emergency! You must stop now, rethink how you are living, change your attitudes, and pay careful attention to diet, exercise, and relaxation.

How did you do?

It's important to find good outlets for your stress. What do you like to do if you have spare time? What hobbies or activities do you enjoy? It's important to know these things before entering nursing school because there will be days when you need to take a break from it all. On those breaks, make sure you are involved in healthy and helpful hobbies or extracurricular activities and not negative ones. Remember that you are a nursing student, and it's important to make sure your image is befitting of the "most trusted profession" on earth. If my loved ones are sick and must be taken care of by you, I would want to be sure that you are someone with upstanding character. I don't want to see my mother's nurse all over social media, intoxicated, looking low, loose, and raggedy. Make sure you are conducting yourself like the person you would want to care for you.

I always tell my students that you can be the smartest one in the room, but people will judge your character and intelligence based on what they see and hear. You may not get the opportunity to prove to them that you actually know your stuff before they pass judgment. Is it necessarily right? No, but it is true! At least for me it is. Of course, you have the right to relax and unwind any way you see fit but just take heed that what you get into while relaxing could come back to haunt you. It could literally make or break whether you are cleared to sit for your licensure exam, the NCLEX.

Stress Warning Signs and Symptoms	
Cognitive Symptoms	**Emotional Symptoms**
▪ Memory problems ▪ Inability to concentrate ▪ Poor judgment ▪ Seeing only the negative ▪ Anxious or racing thoughts ▪ Constant worrying	▪ Moodiness ▪ Irritability or short temper ▪ Agitation, inability to relax ▪ Feeling overwhelmed ▪ Sense of loneliness and isolation ▪ Depression or general unhappiness
Physical Symptoms	**Behavioral Symptoms**
▪ Aches and pains ▪ Diarrhea or constipation ▪ Nausea, dizziness ▪ Chest pain, rapid heartbeat ▪ Loss of sex drive ▪ Frequent colds	▪ Eating more or less ▪ Sleeping too much or too little ▪ Isolating yourself from others ▪ Procrastinating or neglecting responsibilities ▪ Using alcohol, cigarettes, or drugs to relax ▪ Nervous habits (e.g. nail biting, pacing)

Adopted from PNP Slides: Foundations in Nursing Education

Take a look at the chart above. As you can see, stress can cause many symptoms mentally, emotionally, physically, and behaviorally. If you are someone who does not handle stress well, then now is the time to formulate a plan. Find or create a plan for stress management *before* you begin school. If you are already in school, get a plan together for the tough days ahead. Remember that it is okay to talk to someone about your stress. You will feel much better if you have a good outlet for your stress and talking is a good outlet. Other good outlets are exercise, trying new recipes, stress balls for squeezing, a pillow to yell into, getting a good night's sleep, naps on weekends, playing with pets, getting some fresh air on a walk or run, coloring, painting, singing and dancing, just to name a few. When was the last time you colored in a coloring book or danced around being silly with the kids? I'll bet it's been a minute. Try it! I can see you smiling now!

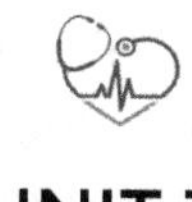

UNIT 12

Professionalism

There are many aspects to professionalism. Some of those aspects include organization, punctuality, time management, communication, self-advocacy, honesty, dependability, and accountability.

Let's begin with organization. In nursing school, the curriculum will move rather quickly. It will be very hard to keep up with the material if everything in your world is a mess. If you are usually a messy person…clean it up. A clean and organized environment are attributes you need to be a good nurse. Your attitude around organization will reflect on your caliber of nursing. Your organizational skills will carry over to everything you do in nursing. Your ability to be organized will help with your system of passing meds, performing treatments, assessing your patients, and documenting nurse's notes in patient charts. Even more so, your ability to be organized will impact the way you interact with your nursing colleagues and doctors. And when it comes to calling doctors about abnormal assessment findings in your patients, believe me, you NEED to be organized. Just try calling a doctor at 3 a.m. after he or she has had a long day in the hospital seeing patients during the coronavirus outbreak, and you don't have your ducks in a row. You *will* probably end up regretting the day you did that. Bottom line is get organized. Your level of organization directly impacts your baseline skills in everything you do as a nurse.

Punctuality and my problem with it almost got me fired from a job in the past. I was bluntly told that if it were not for the caliber of my work, they would have let me go because of my issue with lateness. I was strongly encouraged to fix it. It didn't matter that I had just moved further away from the company and now had a longer commute and that I was stuck in traffic every day. Those excuses were of no consequence when there was a job to be done. The truth is, I have struggled with punctuality my entire life, at least for the past eighteen years anyway. My daughter, Tayah, will vouch for that. Did you catch that? For as long as she has been alive, I have struggled with punctuality. That's terrible. It's actually not a struggle; it's now a very bad habit, one that I work on daily. She was so happy when she got a car and could drive herself around. It makes her very happy to rub it in that she has NEVER been late to school, dance practice, or work since she started driving. We can learn a lot from her. She inherited that quality from my mom (her mom mom). My mom hates to be late, and she seldom ever is. I hate to be late too, and it's not really intentional. I like to maximize the amount of time I am home because I hate to leave my home. I've always been a homebody. I've also always hit my alarm three to four times, which just might have a little to do with my lateness, but I digress. We will talk about alarms a little later. My husband tells me that his father used to tell him growing up that if he was early, then he was on time, and if he was on time, then he was late. That's definitely some good advice.

Nursing students take heed because you absolutely must be on time for class or you will be counted as late and that time adds up very quickly. In nursing school, you are given a finite amount of time you are allowed to miss, and if you go over by even one minute, you will be dismissed from the program. Many students have a problem with this rule. But think about it. . . when you graduate and enter the "real" world, you are given a specific amount of sick time and vacation time. You might not be given both of those categories. Some places give you personal time and tell you to use it as you wish, but basically, you can't go over the specified amount of time or you risk being fired. In healthcare, nurses work twenty-four hours a day. We never leave the patient's side. Meaning if you are the 7 a.m.-3 p.m. shift nurse relieving the night shift nurse, how do you think she would feel if you arrived at 7:05 a.m. and made a habit of it? I'll tell you how she would feel. She would quickly report you to the supervisor's office because she is exhausted and wants to go home and sleep after working all night. ***Tip:*** Most places want the on-coming shift to arrive fifteen minutes before their shift to allow enough time to get a report and do unit rounds before the strike of the hour. That way, you are already in place and ready to go on the hour. If you have a problem like I did, then I implore you to train yourself to wake up thirty minutes earlier.

Okay, here's the alarm talk. Don't keep your alarm next to your bed. Some people put their alarm in their bathroom, so they'll have to get up to turn it off. Once they're up, they just get their day started. Another strategy is to have more than one alarm and set them a couple of minutes behind each other. That way you are so annoyed that you will have no choice but to stay up because you will be turning off alarms for the next five minutes. Get into a habit of being early now, and you'll never be late!

Next up, time management. This is something a lot of nursing students struggle with at first, but once they settle into the semester, they usually find their rhythm. However, I want to bring it to your attention now, so that you realize how important time management is when starting school. Most of the students I've taught have been adult students with jobs and families to juggle before they can even think about settling down to study. That was my story! When I decided to switch careers from business to medical, I was a full-grown adult with a husband and two very young elementary school age children to take care of. There was definitely a huge learning curve to try to manage my studies and my young family. There were many nights that I could not sit down to even begin studying until 9 p.m. I had dinner to make, elementary homework to look over (I swear teachers give the homework to the parents), baths to give, amongst other household duties. I found myself not being able to study until late at night. Did I mention the minimum of two to three hours/night yet? Yes, in nursing school you need to put in two to three hours of study EVERY night, and that's just for starters. As you progress through the program, you will discover that you need more time in order to really grasp certain concepts. Nursing school concepts take time to understand. You will read and re-read and discuss and ponder. Make sure to pencil in enough time in your schedule for all of those activities.

That brings us to communication. I can't stress enough the importance of good communication skills. I realize that it's something we all put on our resumes, but in nursing and healthcare in general, good communication skills are imperative. You will need to communicate with everyone. Not only your fellow nurses on your unit but also with doctors, patients, families of patients, and other people in the facility where you work. Good communication encompasses verbal, non-verbal, and written forms of communication. We could even go a step further and include musical forms of communication. For example, when someone has a stroke, they may lose their ability to speak (left-brained ability), but they can sing (mostly right-brained ability). This happens when the stroke affects one side of the brain and not the other. See, I'm already teaching, and you have barely started school. LOL!

Anyway, back to my point. I'm sure you won't be singing up and down your unit as a form of communication; however, your patient might. The point is that communication comes in many forms, and depending on how you communicate, it can make all the difference in the world with how you are viewed and how you view others.

Of all the people you will be communicating with, the patient is the most important. As a nurse, you are your patient's healthcare advocate. That means that you are always on the side of your patient. Always. It's you and your patient above the family, above the doctor, and even above your own feelings about the situation. We are to make sure our patients are informed of all of their rights, and when they exercise those rights, we are to abide by them. This is where autonomy comes into play. There will be times when you won't agree with the decision your patient is making about their care, but if they are of sound mind and body, then they have the right to make any decision they see fit. It may not be the best decision in your eyes or even their family's eyes, but it is their right. As the nurse, you must be an advocate. Being an advocate also means that you make sure your patient is well-informed of any consequences, but after that, the decision is in their hands. There may be times when you will struggle with your own morals against what your patient believes. In those instances, it's important that you seek out counseling on how to reconcile your own feelings about the situation. Most places of employment have professionals on staff, and if they don't, then they have organizations that are included in your healthcare package that can help.

We've discussed your role as the patient's advocate but guess who else's advocate you are. That's right, yours. Self-advocacy is a skill you must learn and become comfortable with. If you don't care about you, no one else will. Self-advocacy takes a certain level of assertiveness. In order to have your needs met, you must master the art of speaking up for yourself. Speaking up for yourself first involves identifying your needs, figuring out how best to meet those needs, and lastly, finding a way to put it all into action. Activating your needs may involve the help of other people. You must identify the people who can help and enlist those people as part of your self-advocacy plan. Teachers, friends, family members, and supervisors may be some of those people on your list. Remember that when telling people what you need, you should have clearly defined expectations, noting any boundaries or areas that are off limits. Then, when the time comes to call on those people, you must be willing to put your plan into action. Having a plan does nothing unless you are willing to act on it.

It's time to talk about honesty. Honesty is when you speak the truth and act truthfully. Nursing is a profession where honesty genuinely matters. Always be honest when it comes to your nursing career. Be honest with the patient, the staff, and the facility you work for. That said, there is a skill to being honest. You can be honest and express it in a way that isn't helpful. Some people don't possess the skill of compassion. If you know you don't have that skill, then seek coaching before having to deliver a certain type of news to your patient. I believe that most of us got into this great profession because of our compassion for others. Being honest utilizes our ability to show compassion.

I mentioned the importance of punctuality earlier in this section, and part of being dependable is arriving for your shift at the scheduled time. In nursing, it is advisable to show up *before* your shift starts. This allows time to get what's called, report. Report includes any necessary discussions about the patients and other critical happenings that occurred during the shift. Showing up ahead of your scheduled shift ensures that the off-going nurse can leave on time. You will expect the same when it's time for you to end your shift. There will also be times when you must depend on your coworkers to help when dealing with challenging patients or difficult tasks that you can't do alone. When you are that dependable nurse, then others will certainly be dependable for you. You will grow to love your team. It's that love and team spirit that kept me at certain jobs for as long as I stayed. I loved my coworkers. If anyone from PH is reading this, you know who you are, and I really do miss the good times working there with an exceptional and dependable team. I can't stress enough the importance of being a dependable nurse. Remember you will be part of a team and you must approach your job with a team mentality. As a team member, everyone depends on each other for help in some way every day. Remember to be a good team member because you will need your team, and they will need you.

Last but not least is accountability. Nurses live and work by a code. It's called the code of ethics. When you graduate from nursing school, whether LPN or RN, you will have to take an oath. That oath is expressed in the code of ethics. It is a public declaration of the standards you swear to uphold as a nurse. According to the code of ethics of the American Nurses Association (ANA), "Accountability means to be answerable to oneself and others for one's own actions." Accountability in nursing requires nurses to follow an ethical conduct code based on the "principles of fidelity and respect for the dignity, worth, and self-determination of patients." You can connect with the ANA and read all about accountability along with other characteristics in our Nurses Code of Ethics at the following link. www.nursingworld.org/ana/about-ana/standards/.

To help you maintain accountability, I suggest you find an accountability partner or team. We need people who we will answer to and people who will answer to us. An accountability partner or team isn't necessarily an authoritative figure but more like a friend who will lovingly correct you if and when you need it. An accountability partner will also help you if you have veered off the right path. Accountability simply means that you will be responsible for your actions and your words.

Being accountable to someone is an important component in our growth. It also helps keep us grounded and humbled, so we can continue to do a great job of helping patients and our team.

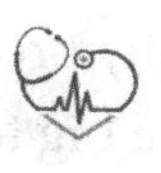

UNIT 13

Nursing School Is Work

Just being honest, there may be days that you want to quit. You will go through every reason in your mind, simply searching for the justification to quit. DON'T! You must enter nursing school with this thought: There will be tough days, it's going to be a lot of work. You might struggle juggling it all, and you will have tests coming back to back. It will seem like you don't have time to study, and family problems and emergencies will arise on the evening before a big test. You must learn to anticipate these things; it's called life. It's life on life's terms. If you master the art of anticipating these things, when the thoughts or problems occur, you won't be caught off guard.

Let's discuss the types of work you will encounter in nursing school. There's studying, reviewing, practicing, researching, reading, and quizzing. You will have PowerPoint slides, textbooks, web resources, and journal articles. Complete reading assignments before class and come to class prepared to ask questions and participate in class discussions. You will be doing a lot of NCLEX style questions for review, reading some and skimming some of the chapters in the textbook, working on group projects, researching agencies, presenting reports on cultural and religious backgrounds, practicing skills and techniques before you are tested on them in the lab, making note cards and creating study materials, using apps and computer platforms, doing care-plans which can be four to five pages long, studying two to three hours a night, researching patient charts and concept maps, writing out medication logs, and the list goes on. In addition to your schoolwork, some of you may have little ones and husbands or wives to take care of. Therefore, you can see there is lots of work to be done. Hang in there through the problems and issues that come up; keep studying and putting the time in and stay positive throughout your journey. Good things and new opportunities are right around the corner.

UNIT 14

Other Obligations Can Hinder Your Success

Let's discuss your job. Many of you are certified nursing assistants (CNAs), patient care technicians (PCTs), nurse's aides (NAs), or even medication technicians or medication aides (MAs). As I mentioned before, it's difficult going to school while trying to maintain full-time employment. When I first started nursing school back in 2007, the director of the program told us that if we worked more than twenty hours per week, it would be very difficult to successfully complete the program. I soon realized how true that statement was. Fortunately, I had a husband that encouraged me to focus on school while he "brought home the bacon." I did have a small summer camp and after school camp position at the time, but it was nothing to write home about. However, it did keep gas in the car and food on the table, so I didn't complain. I was grateful to have non-strenuous employment that allowed me to work on my dreams. I was also raising five and six-year-old daughters at the time, and all of us mothers, aunties, nanas, me-maws, pop- pops, and da-das can attest that raising kids is really the most difficult full-time job. Nonetheless, I was blessed to have children so close in age that they were each other's company many a day when I needed to crack my books open to study. Although most of my study time was done from 9 p.m. to 1 a.m., I was thankful for the days my husband was off, so I was able to take more advantage of daylight study time. I am telling you what I was told all those years ago. If you're working a lot of hours, it will be extremely hard to be successful in any nursing program. It's not impossible, but it is difficult.

Once I had a student who said that her job was making her work forty hours per week. They denied her the opportunity to work only weekends, so that she could focus on her studies during the week. She was very upset about it. I asked her if she was in nursing school to become a nurse *or* to remain a CNA? After giving some thought to what we discussed, she quit her job. I never intended for her to go to that extent, but she really took the time to think about what I said and decided that nursing school needed lots of focus and attention. She wanted to become a nurse. Therefore, for her, quitting her job was the logical decision. She took stock of her resources and decided that it was doable.

If you have a way of decreasing the number of hours you work or for a short period of time taking a leave of absence or only working a few hours on the weekends, then take it. Yes, you have other responsibilities. The bills still need to get paid. Your kids still need to eat. You still need to be able to put gas in your car; I get it. But if there is an opportunity to reduce your work hours therefore reducing your stress and increasing your study time, do it! Look for ways to become resourceful as discussed in Unit 4 of this book.

As I discussed earlier, take stock in your resources before entering school. What do you have in your savings account? Can you take in a roommate? Can your parents, siblings, or a friend watch your kids for free until you start making money working as a nurse? Can you buy off-brand food and clothing to save money? Can you stock your cabinets before attending nursing school, or shop in bulk to save money? Can you carpool to save on gas money? Can you cut out unnecessary bills like cable and get a Roku to save money? There are plenty of money-saving tricks out there. If you start to use your noodle, I'm sure you can accomplish a few of these tips. I'm certain you are very resourceful!

Here is a big point that will help change your life. You must master this concept. It will help you for the rest of your life and not just in nursing school. Master the art, and it most definitely is an art, of saying...NO! "No is a complete sentence. It does not require satisfaction or an explanation." I am not sure where this quote originated, but I like it and give credit to the person who made this revelation. I think it frees a lot of people up. There are many books out there written on the art of saying no. If you are a people pleaser, you might want to pick one up some time. I'm sure it will change your life.

I am speaking from a woman's perspective, of course, but no doubt some men may suffer from the same disease. I call it a disease because it is. It's "the disease to please." If you want to maintain your sanity while in nursing school, then you should be "practicing on your art" (Thank you Dragon Fly Jones, a character from *Martin*, the best show of the 90s.)

As women, we are natural caretakers and people pleasers. We want everyone to be happy and we want everyone to like us. Well, honey chile, let me tell you. You need to let go of that notion! Do what you have to do and begin to change the way you are programmed. I'll let you in on a little secret. Everyone is not going to be happy, and everyone is not going to like you. Master this new way of thinking now, then when you encounter someone with a nasty attitude and you can't figure out why, it won't come as a surprise to you that everyone is not going to be happy, and everyone is not going to like you. And that is okay!

You will have coworkers, the patient's family members, and even patients that don't like you. I always say, "That sounds like a personal problem to me." It took me a while to learn that I am not entitled to know nor should I concern myself with how people feel about me. I just need to treat everyone cordially enough to work with them, so together we can care for our patients. If the patient does not like you, you can try to swap them with another nurse and pick up a patient in return, but you should really try to get to the bottom of the issue. Most of the time it is something they are dissatisfied with, and you are able to fix it or solve the problem. The misunderstanding is as simple as solving the problem. If it's not that simple or the patient is uncomfortable with you, then go ahead and switch with another nurse.

I believe our disease to please begins somewhere in childhood. Women are taught to be good homemakers, good mothers, good friends, and the list goes on. This mentality of making sure everything is just right for everyone else, sometimes at the expense of our own selves, is a disease. Disease = Dis Ease. We have dis ease in our bodies when things are not right with us, causing us to feel uneasy. This uneasiness can be due to any number of factors. It can be outside forces, influences, and situations that make us feel uneasy and cause us emotional, physical, psychological, or spiritual suffering. Please don't feed your dis ease, but starve it. When you starve something, it will eventually die. We want that mentality to die. When something dies, it leaves room for new birth. Tell me, what's inside of you waiting to be birthed?

UNIT 15

Goodbye to Your Social Life

Don't totally freak out by the title of this unit. But yes, that's right, say goodbye to having a social life. If you want to be a nurse, then say goodbye to a social life for a little while. There's just no time. You have a lot to learn and a little time to learn it. Remember, this is only temporary!

Tell your friends to bear with you because you won't be able to hang out for long periods of time for about a good year depending on the type of nursing program you are in. Nursing takes up a lot of your time and attention. In order to succeed in school, you must give nursing the time it needs. If you are to succeed in school, you have to cement these facts into your mind! This reminds me of the time our oldest daughter, Sabria, told me that when she was in school working on her master's in psychology, her friends who were studying nursing could never hang out with the crew. Again, don't freak out, but anything worth having in life is worth the sacrifice. In nursing school, you will sacrifice most of your play time for work. I say most because there may be small occasions when you can squeeze in some time for extracurricular activities, but there is not much, so use your time wisely.

When you explain to your friends that you don't have much time to hang out, make sure they know that you still love them, but you absolutely must focus on your education for the foreseeable future. You are making a huge change in your life that has the ability to take your family out of poverty and into the middle class; therefore, school deserves your undivided attention. If they want to hang out, suggest they come over to help you study. Better yet, convince them to go to school with you! There have been plenty of students who have done that. Imagine the huge accomplishment and sense of pride in walking across the stage with your friend(s) to receive your diplomas together. That's priceless! But if they don't join you in this endeavor, they can certainly come over to help you study. Make up some sandwiches and give them something to drink. You may not be able to hangout like you used to, but you can still share a meal together while they help you study, of course. The bottom line is you must *really* study. There is no time to waste when you're in nursing school. Time is a most precious commodity. Once it's gone, you will never get it back.

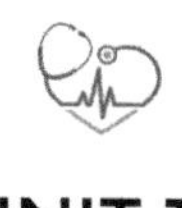

UNIT 16

Attending Clinicals

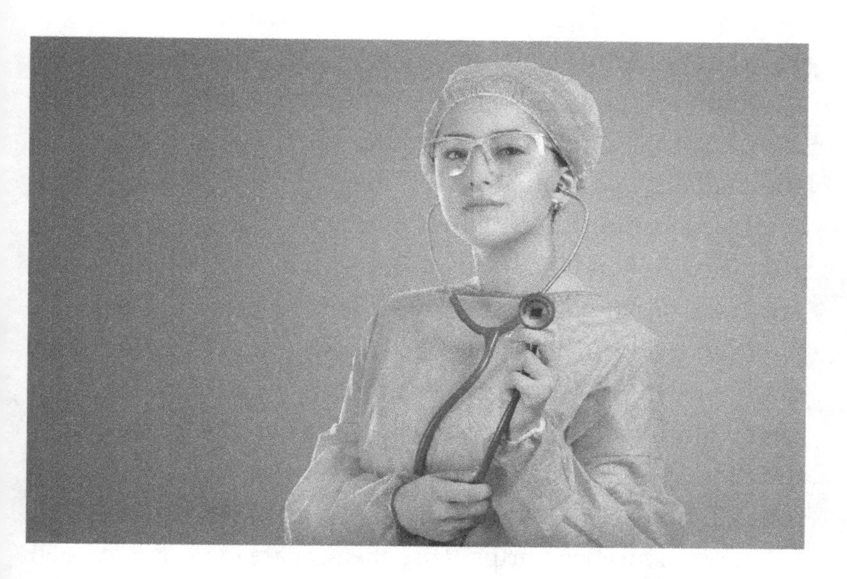

Nursing school is much more than just sitting in a classroom taking notes. The type of nursing school program you are enrolled in will determine if you will attend clinicals. Clinical is the hands-on training part of nursing school. It is where you get experience while you are a student.

Programs that include clinicals are great because you get to apply what you've learned in class to the real world. Most of these types of programs are LPN/LVN programs. LPN stands for Licensed Practical Nurse. LVN stands for Licensed Vocational Nurse. The terms are interchangeable, and their use depends on which state you live in. As a beginner, these programs give you a great foundation in nursing. You will gain classroom theory hours, which you will use immediately when you attend clinical. Studies show that one of the best ways people learn is by doing. Hands-on skills while you go to school will prepare you for an entry level position in nursing. LPN/LVN programs do a great job of helping you become good at bedside nursing. What I mean by that is you will gain a great education as a beginner nurse. The skills you will learn are the basic hands-on tasks that are foundational to nursing practice also known as nursing skills. These nursing skills are the foundation to nursing practice since these are the skills that you will use throughout your career. Most of the skills are taught in the school's lab, while other skills are taught in the clinical area. I will expand on these areas in more detail in my next book. To keep up with all things RISCQ by TALONDA, visit my website https://riscqhealthcare.com on a regular basis for information and tools to help you along your journey. For now, I will provide a laundry list of the skills just to give you an idea of all the fun stuff you will be learning. Of course, this is not the complete list, but it will give you a good idea of some of the duties of an LPN. If you are considering a four-year college to earn a BSN or entering an associate's program, working toward an ASN/ADN, you will begin with these same concepts plus many more.

Like I said, these are some of the skills you will learn in school. It's certainly not exhaustive, but this will give you a good idea of what an entry level nurse does. I will go into further detail in my next book.

Safety
Using bed and chair
Monitors
Using restraints: belt, mitt, vest, wrist, ankle
Proper disposal of sharps, hazardous waste
Proper height for patient procedures
Patient environment: lowering bed, clearing clutter
Teaching patient to use call bell

Surgical Care
Teaching patient to cough, deep breathe, leg exercises
Applying: anti-embolism stockings, sequential compression devices

Surgical Asepsis
Sterile gloving
Setting up a sterile field

Medical Asepsis
Hand hygiene
Donning (putting on) Personal Protective Equipment (PPE)
Doffing (taking off) Personal Protective Equipment (PPE)

Urinary Elimination
Indwelling Urinary/Foley Catheter: inserting, discontinuing, irrigation
Inserting an Intermittent Urinary Catheter (straight catheter)
Applying an External Condom Catheter
Measuring urine output: Foley, bedpan, urinal
Measuring Post Void Residual (PVR) with a Bladder Scanner
Obtaining a sterile urine specimen from catheter

Medication Preparation
Drawing up medication from vials
Preparing and insulin pen

Wound Care
Applying and removing drying dressings and bandages
Irrigating a wound
Emptying a closed wound drainage system
Removing staples from a healed incision
Dressing a wound (sterile technique)

Health Assessment
Performing head-to-toe assessment
Interviewing patient on admission
Documentation

Vital Signs
Taking temperature: oral, axillary, rectal, temporal, tympanic
Taking a pulse (heart rate): peripheral, apical, apical-radial
Assessing respirations
Measuring blood pressure

Diagnostic Testing
Obtaining blood sugar via fingerstick
Performing Venipuncture

Hygiene
Providing a bed
Bath
Perineal care
Foot care
Oral care
Making an occupied bed

Nutrition
Nasogastric Tube: Inserting, discontinuing, removal
Administer feedings through Gastric and Enteric tubes (infusion pump and by gravity)
Spiking new feeding set
Managing Gastric Suction: Equipment set-up, emptying suction container, irrigating nasogastric tubing
Feeding patient with Dementia or behavioral issues
Checking placement and residual of Gastrostomy Tubes

Oxygenation
Administering oxygen therapy
Performing Tracheostomy care: changing outer cannula and suctioning
Naso and Oropharyngeal suctioning

Moving and Positioning
Moving patient in bed: one and two-assist
Assisting with Ambulation
Transferring patient: bed to stretcher, bed to chair
Operating a Hoyer Lift (Observed in clinical)
Performing passive range of motion
Logrolling a patient

Medication Administration
Medication guidelines for ALL medications
Medication Administration:
* PO (by mouth) pills and liquids
* Buccal (in the cheek)
* Sublingual (under the tongue)
* Subcutaneous (in fat)
* IM (Intramuscular) traditional and Z track method
* Transdermal (through the skin)
* Intradermal (under the skin)
* Instillation (into a body cavity or orifice)
* Rectally (into the rectum)
* Inhalation (inhaled into the lungs)
* Ophthalmic (into the eyes)
* Otic (into the ears)
* Nasally (in the nares)
* IM (Infant first shot)
* IV (intravenous)
    Using: Piggyback Administration set - Gravity Infusion and Infusion Pump
    Initiating Peripheral Venipuncture
    Spiking a new bag of fluid
    Peripheral IV dressings: administrating and discontinuing

Bowel Elimination
Ostomy Care: changing and cleaning the stoma
Administering a cleansing enema
Helping patient use a bedpan
Emptying a bedpan

Pain Management
Setting up and maintaining Patient Controlled Analgesia (PCA) by pump

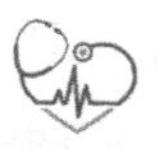

UNIT 17

Tests, Tests, and More Tests

You will have many tests in nursing school. The best piece of advice I can give you is to be prepared by studying. Prioritize what's most important to study by paying attention in class, noting any themes the instructor repeats or stresses. You can also be aware of what to study by noting anything in your notes that is capitalized or bolded. Part of being prepared is to know your objectives. Objectives are usually listed on the outline or syllabus. Your objectives tell you what we expect you to know after the course is completed. If you can answer each of the objectives, then it's a good indication that you are prepared to take your test. You will have many tests because it's the only way to evaluate if you are learning the content.

Some of the types of tests consist of unit exams, pharmacology exams, hands-on testing, and proctored exams. Unit exams are exactly what they sound like, tests that are administered at the end of each unit. Pharmacology exams are tests you will take concerning medication knowledge. Pharmacology tests include basic math and simple algebra because you will need to know how to calculate the proper amount of medication to administer to your patients. These tests also assess your actual medication knowledge, meaning the characteristics of the medication itself. You will need to know the generic, trade name, classification, action, side effects, and nursing interventions associated with medications. These tests will also assess your ability to read medication labels. Hands-on tests are evaluations of your skills in the lab. We evaluate how well you know what you are doing by assessing you in the lab area. This includes administering medications, sterile gloving, foley insertion, and taking vital signs, just to name a few.

The last type of testing is proctored assessments or exams. A proctored exam is one that is given via the computer. It is a timed assessment. These proctored assessments are good practice for what it will be like to take the NCLEX exam at the end of your program. It is given in the presence of a person or more than one person called a proctor. The proctor is responsible for starting and stopping the exam, fixing problems, and monitoring students for issues that arise, including cheating during the exam. You will receive your score directly after the test is over, which is a nice benefit for students. It allows the instructor to know which areas you are lacking knowledge or understanding in and where reinforced teaching needs to take place. Another nice feature is that you, the student, are also able to pull up reports that show you the areas you need to brush up on. Some reports even lead you to the exact chapter and page number where the information you missed is found to help make your study time more efficient. Again, I will go into further detail in my next book. Check my website https://riscqhealthcare.com to sign up for webinars and specialized teaching sessions that will help you pass your tests, including the NCLEX. Space will be limited, so get on my email list to make sure you are among the first to receive information for special promotions I have that can benefit you.

UNIT 18

Your Learning Style

A learning style refers to the preferred way in which someone processes, understands, and retains information; it's basically how you learn best. Learning styles can depend on environment, emotion, experience, strengths, and many other factors. Do you know what your learning style is? There are many learning styles, and I encourage you to explore this concept before entering school. And if you can't look into it before starting school, don't worry. It will become apparent to you once you begin to sit in classes, listen to lectures, and take part in labs and other activities. You will begin to gather and discover information about yourself that is helpful for figuring out which learning style(s) you fall under.

If you have the time, there are assessments that can help you determine your learning style. The one I found most useful was educationplanner.org. If you would like to take the assessment, here is the link: www.educationplanner.org/students/self-assessments/learning-styles.shtml. The assessment is only twenty short questions, and your results are available immediately. Narrowing down and pinpointing your learning styles will save you time and frustration because the results will tell you exactly what you should be doing to maximize your learning experience. You will discover that you learn well in some situations and learn better from some instructors' teaching styles over others. Everyone doesn't fit into the same box. Discovering your learning style is also important to your instructor. It allows them to meet the needs of everyone in the class.

Learning styles can also help you determine an effective study method, ensuring you get the most out of your study time. You will try many different methods of studying in school. Knowing your learning style can help narrow down some of those methods by helping you come up with a list of study modalities, allowing you to gain the most from your study time.

Check out the results from my assessment. My results show that I am mainly a visual learner. Being a visual learner means I primarily do well with a lot of colorful diagrams, making note cards to study, and writing down keywords, ideas, and instructions. My results tell me that I should sit near the front of the class in order to minimize distractions. The assessment also provided other suggestions on how to do well as a visual learner. The assessment results also show that I am an auditory learner. That means that I do well hearing the lesson. As you can see in my results, my visual and auditory results are pretty much tied. This means I can benefit from both learning styles.

Below are the results I received from www.educationplanner.org/students/self-assessments/learning-styles.shtml.

* The link to my results is https://bit.ly/2zJS2Xp

What's Your Learning Style? The Results

Your scores:

- Auditory: 45%
- Visual: 50%
- Tactile: 5%

You are a **visual** learner! Check out the information below, or view all of the learning styles.

Visual

If you are a visual learner, you learn by reading or seeing pictures. You understand and remember things by sight. You can picture what you are learning in your head, and you learn best by using methods that are primarily visual. You like to see what you are learning.

As a visual learner, you are usually neat and clean. You often close your eyes to visualize or remember something, and you will find something to watch if you become bored. You may have difficulty with spoken directions and may be easily distracted by sounds. You are attracted to color and to the spoken language (like stories) that is rich in imagery.

Here are some things that visual learners like you can do to learn better:

- Sit near the front of the classroom. (It won't mean you're the teacher's pet!)
- Have your eyesight checked on a regular basis.
- Use flashcards to learn new words.
- Try to visualize things that you hear or things that are read to you.
- Write down key words, ideas, or instructions.
- Draw pictures to help explain new concepts and then explain the pictures.
- Color code things.
- Avoid distractions during study times.

Remember that you need to see things, not just hear things, to learn well.

Make an effort to take the short assessment. Knowing your learning style will go a long way to help you while in nursing school.

Just a side note: Knowing my learning style versus my children's learning styles helps me be a better mother-teacher. Yes, I just made that up. What I mean is that there was a time when my youngest daughter, Rena, and I would butt heads over her homework. I didn't understand why she couldn't understand what I thought were "simple" concepts. I would get frustrated with her and yell, assuming that she just wasn't putting in the effort. As a result, she became upset and resentful of my teaching style or lack thereof. As she progressed through school, I would wonder why she never asked me for help. She never told me when she needed help with her homework because she internalized my yelling as me not having enough patience to help her. Rena didn't divulge this to me until last year. What I thought was laziness turned out to be a learning disability (different learning ability). Praise God I have a sister who was a guidance counselor at the time. Thanks, Aesha! She encouraged me to have Rena tested. The results showed that there was a true issue with how Rena processes information. I felt like such a horrible mother.

Rena learns best by doing. She is a tactile learner. Something told me she wasn't an auditory learner for sure. I'll bet a lot of parents think the same thing about their children. My point is that if I had just taken the time to check myself, get some patience, and do some further investigation into her issues, I would have known about her needs as a learner. I'm so happy she finally confided in me. This experience has made me use a different approach with my son.

So, parents, while we are homeschooling our children during this coronavirus pandemic, take the time to find out the learning styles of your children. It would not only help them, but it would help us by saving us the time in trying to figure out what study methods are the most helpful.

UNIT 19

Rest and Relaxation

It's so important to get your rest woman! It's so important to get your rest man! What do you usually do for relaxation? As discussed earlier, when I spoke about stress, it's important to have positive outlets that will help you relax. Is it the beach? Is it curling up with a good book? Resting in your hammock? Snuggling with your pooch or kitty? Sunbathing in the yard? Whatever it is, be sure to set time aside to do it. Yes, it's of the utmost importance to study to be prepared for class and tests, but it's equally important to be able to clear your mind by relaxing and resting.

Don't neglect actual sleep. Set a good bedtime and try to stick to it. Getting enough sleep is actually good for stress because it decreases cortisol levels (the stress hormone). Cortisol is that horrible hormone responsible for putting this fat around my stomach. The more consistent sleep you get, the more your body will get used to knowing that you will give it what it needs. This can literally help you by decreasing harmful cortisol levels. Cortisol has many great benefits too, but in high levels, it's not good for your body.

Don't forget your spiritual life. You should, you must, and you need to begin your day with spiritual guidance or silent meditation. Take it from me that starting your day in a prayerful or silent meditation mode will do a lot for helping you to have a good day. I find that my day is so much better. I have zero road rage, which is always good. I can deal with other people's stupidity better when I am prayed up, and it just puts me in a better mood. Imagine going long periods of time without water. How long do you think you would survive? And if you think you only need water on Monday's or when you feel thirsty, you would be mistaken. Just as your body needs water all the time, your spirit and your soul need prayer all the time. Don't neglect your spiritual life.

Starting your day with prayer or meditation will also allow you to be in control of your emotions, instead of allowing your emotions to control you. In my opinion, you should never begin your day with social media, the news, or emails. These platforms are full of distractions. They can make you feel abnormal, angry, or anxious, respectively. Checking in with these platforms before checking in with your own feelings when you first wake up is not the best way to start your day. Do yourself and your family a favor. Start your day with a few moments of silence. Twenty minutes is sufficient. Take your time arising and then begin your morning routine. Your morning routine might begin with a shower, a workout, or a stroll to the kitchen for a nice hot cup of tea or coffee. No matter what your routine, make sure you are in command of the start of your day. You can thank me later.

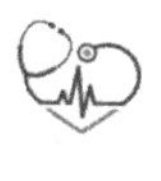

UNIT 20

The Best Career Choice

Take comfort in knowing that after you have digested everything that was said in this book, you have made the best career choice. I am a champion for all things nursing. You are in the right place at the right time. This career will elevate your life to new levels. This career will propel you from poverty into the middle class. We are still one of the only disciplines with a very easy way to enter. Some disciplines are quite jealous of us. What I mean is that entry into the nursing field only requires a diploma from an accredited program, which is usually as little as twelve to fifteen months long. And then with the passing of your NCLEX-PN, you are on your way in the profession. I spoke about the different career paths in the first unit of this book, but here is a little information about choosing the direction you'd like to take. You can start at other levels like attending a two-year associate's program that is structured like many LPN programs. The difference is that instead of a diploma, you will get a degree. The associate of science in nursing (ASN) is the name of one. Like LPN programs, these programs also give you hands-on training while in nursing school. Another alternative method of entry into the nursing field is to enter a four-year degree program with a college or university and then sit for the NCLEX-RN. Your four-year degree might be a bachelor of science in health science. It's important to remember that it's great to graduate from a program, but you still need to take and pass the NCLEX to become a licensed nurse. When I mentioned that other disciplines are "jealous (my opinion) of nursing," it's because other professions can have much higher standards of entry into their fields. There are many who would love to begin working in their chosen fields much sooner, but they can't. For instance, the entry level into the profession of physical therapy currently requires a doctorate degree. I know this because my baby, Tayah, will begin as a freshman at Alvernia University in the physical therapy program in the fall of 2020. They are structured in such a way that she already knows it will take her six years to complete her studies. When she completes her program, she will have a bachelor of science in health science after four years and her doctor of physical therapy after the entire six years. I can't wait to call her Doctor Rogers. To continue gushing about my children, in another year from now, my daughter Rena will attend West Chester University following in my and her oldest sister's footsteps. I am very proud of all of my girls. Okay, gushing over! Part of the reason why nurses are afforded this privilege is because of the huge, worldwide shortage of nurses. The goal is to get as many people educated and trained as soon as possible to help fill the gaps in society. People are older and sicker because people are living much longer than they once did. Currently, there are not enough nurses to care for them. As far as I'm concerned, why wouldn't everyone want to be a nurse? It's not just a job; it's a career. There are many different places you can work as a nurse and such a variety of opportunities in the nursing field. There is limitless potential, basically a never-ending career ladder.

You will never stop learning as a nurse. According to the latest evidence-based practice (EBP), the medical profession, pertaining to patient care, is constantly changing. That means that some things that were done in nursing years ago are no longer the best and safest way to do them. Based on real-life patient reactions, path of healing, or positive and negative outcomes, medicine continues to change and evolve. Example: Years ago, nurses and/or doctors never wore gloves. Today, we wouldn't think about doing some aspects of patient care without wearing gloves. Of course, not everything requires gloves, but the messy stuff does.

As stated in the introduction of this book, nursing is still the number one trusted profession. Not even doctors have this honor. The patients trust us sometimes with their deepest secrets. Things that they can't tell their families, they might tell you. It's important that if and when they share something with you, you act with integrity. Integrity, simply put, means that you are honest, you have morals, and as such you honor your word. Remember, you are the patient's advocate. You are not there to please the doctor or the family but to let the patient know that you will do everything you can to help meet their needs. That's why they trust us.

Nursing is not to be entered into lightly. You can't do this career for the money. Yes, you will make good money, but if something else deeper inside of you is not calling you to be a nurse, then the money motivation will soon get old. I once took a job for money. I should say what I thought was good money. Later, I discovered that with all of the problems and stress it brought me, it just wasn't worth it. I hated my job. I was relieved to finally let that position go. I vowed that I would NEVER take a position for money alone again.

The lesson I learned from that time in my life was that peace of mind is more valuable to me than money. I stress "to me" because I am sensitive to the fact that someone else might be able to sacrifice their peace of mind to make a larger income, depending on the individual circumstances. We adults know that life is not always easy, and we must prioritize in order of importance. That is a personal decision. For me, I haven't looked back. I even accepted a position in nursing that paid me much less than I was worth in order to gain valuable experience that I knew I needed to help me move forward in my career path. Life is like that. You win, you lose, you adjust, and you reboot accordingly. Your ability to recognize and do those things will carry you far in life and your career. So, welcome to the beginning of the rest of your life as you embark on an educational experience that will prepare you to be an excellent nurse.

APPENDIX

Important Websites in Nursing

National Council of State Boards of Nursing (NCSBN)

- NCSBN is an independent, 501(c)(3) not-for-profit organization.
- All state boards of nursing belong to it.
- Develops nursing licensure exams.
- Involved in the safe regulation of nursing.
- www.ncsbn.org/Pennsylvania.htm

The National League for Nursing (NLN)

- Dedicated to excellence in nursing, the National League for Nursing is the premier organization for nurse faculty and leaders in nursing education.
- The NLN offers professional development, networking opportunities, testing services, nursing research grants, and public policy initiatives to its 40,000 individual and 1,200 institutional members.

- NLN members represent nursing education programs across the spectrum of higher education, health care organizations, and agencies.
- www.nln.org/accreditation-services/the-nln-commission-for-nursing-education-accreditation-(cnea)/overview

Pennsylvania Code and Bulletin

- Lists the functions of the LPN
- www.pacodeandbulletin.gov/Display/pacode?file=/secure/pacode/data/049/chapter21/s21.145.html

National Association of Licensed Practical Nurses (NALPN)

- NALPN provides leadership for the nearly one million licensed practical and vocational nurses employed in the United States.
- NALPN encourages every LPN and LVN to make continuing education a priority for the purpose of personal growth and improved patient care.
- NALPN achieves recognition of LPNs and LVNs and advocates the effective utilization of licensed practical and vocational nurses in every type of healthcare facility.

- NALPN interprets the role and function of the LPN and LVN for the public in order to win greater understanding and appreciation of the contribution of practical/vocational nursing to the nation's healthcare system.
- NALPN represents practical/vocational nursing through relationships with other national nursing, medical and allied health organizations, legislators, government officials, health agencies and institutions, educators and other professional groups which share the common goal of improved patient care.
- NALPN serves as the central source of information on what is new and changing in practical/vocational nursing education and practice on the local, state, and national levels.
- https://nalpn.org/

National Federation of Licensed Practical Nurses, Inc. (NFLPN)

- Improve education and nursing care
- Promotes continuing education
- Certification exams for LPNs
- Foot care, intravenous therapy, gerontology

- Interprets the role and functions of the www.nflpn.org
- This is the Official Professional Organization for LPN/LVN.

National Association for Practical Nurse Education and Service (NAPNES)

- Promotes and defends practical nursing practice
- Strives to improve practical nursing education
- Provides continuing education and certifications
- Pharmacology, long-term care, and intravenous therapy
- Publishes the NAPNES Forum and *Journal of Practical Nursing*
- Has an annual convention
- www.napnes.org

RN Continuing Education Credits

- They offer most state-required nurse licensure courses and are a featured PACE provider for CCMC nursing education courses.
- They also offer competency assessments, content licensing, group CE discounts and even the latest in nursing news and other resources for nursing professionals.

- RN Continuing Education | Find Nurse CE Courses at RN.com
- www.rn.com/nursing-education/

Nursing Continuing Education

- Alternative site for obtaining nursing CEs (RNs)
- www.nursingce.com/

The American Association of Colleges of Nursing (AACN)

- The national voice for academic nursing
- Influences the nursing profession to improve healthcare
- Promotes public support for professional nursing education, research, and AACN works to establish quality standards for nursing education
- Assists schools in implementing practice
- AACN Fact Sheet - DNP

American Nursing Association (ANA)

- Their mission is to lead the profession to shape the future of nursing and healthcare.

- Improve patient care through supporting both individuals and organizations to advance the nursing profession
- Advocate in Congress
- Set the bar for credentialing worldwide
- The ANA Enterprise exists to give every nurse the best chance of success
- www.nursingworld.org

American Nurses Credentialing Center (ANCC)

- The American Nurses Credentialing Center (ANCC) credentials both organizations and individuals who advance nursing practice whether you want to boost your career prospects or achieve international recognition for your healthcare organization.
- www.nursingworld.org/ancc/

American Nurses Association Foundation (ANA Foundation)

- Is the philanthropic arm of the American Nurses Association (ANA)
- Elevating the profession of nursing globally
- Engaging all nurses to ensure professional success

- Evolving the practice of nursing to transform health and healthcare.
- www.nursingworld.org/foundation/

American Nurses Enterprise (ANA Enterprise)

- The ANA Enterprise is the family of companies that comprise the American Nurses Association (ANA), the American Nurses Credentialing Center (ANCC), and the American Nurses Foundation.
- The ANA Enterprise leverages the combined strength of each to drive excellence in practice and ensure nurses' voices and vision are recognized by policy leaders, industry influencers, and employers. From professional development and advocacy to credentialing and grants, the ANA Enterprise is the leading resource for nurses to equip themselves with the tools, information, and network they need to excel in their individual practices. In helping individual nurses succeed — across all practices and specialties, and at each stage of their careers — the ANA Enterprise is lighting the way for the entire profession to succeed.
- www.nursingworld.org/ana-enterprise/

REFERENCES

All book images taken from Pixabay.com. Free download.

American Nurses Association. (2020). Code of Ethics for Nurses. www.nursingworld.org/ana/about-ana/standards/.

Education Planner.org. (2020). What's Your Learning Style? The Results. Retrieved on June 25, 2020 from, www.educationplanner.org/students/self-assessments/learning-styles.shtml.

Ericksen, K. (2017). The Importance of Critical Thinking Skills in Nursing. Retrieved on June, 25, 2020 from, www.rasmussen.edu/degrees/nursing/blog/understanding-why-nurses-need-critical-thinking-skills/.

Hurst, K. (2013-2020). Manifestation Guide: How to Manifest Anything You Want in 24 hrs. Retrieved on April 30, 2020 from, www.thelawofattraction.com/manifest-something-want-24hrs-less/.

Kurzen, C. (2017). Contemporary Practical/Vocational Nursing. (8th Ed.). Wolters Kluwer.

NIH US. National Library of Medicine. (2020). Antibody titer blood test. Retrieved on May 15, 2020 from, https://medline-plus.gov/ency/article/003333.htm.

Practical Nursing Program (PNP) Slides. Foundations in Nursing Education. (n.d). Stress Warning Signs and Symptoms. Retrieved March 5, 2020 from, https://pnp-moodle.cciu.org/course/view.php?id=58

Segal, S., Smith, M., Segal, R., and Robinson, L. (2020). Stress Symptoms, Signs, and Causes. Retrieved on May 1, 2020 from, www.helpguide.org/articles/stress/stress-symptoms-signs-and-causes.htm.

Writers, S. (2019, December 19). 6 Things to Know About the NCLEX Examination. Retrieved June 26, 2020, from https://nursejournal.org/articles/6-things-to-know-about-the-nclex-examination/.

ABOUT THE AUTHOR

Talonda S. Rogers is a nurse instructor for the Practical Nursing Program at the Chester County Intermediate Unit in Downingtown, PA, and holds a master of science in nursing education from West Chester University. Prior to entering the healthcare field, she received a bachelor of science in marketing from West Chester University. Talonda works for the very program where she started her career as an LPN back in 2007, and she is the founder of RISCQ by TALONDA Healthcare Consultants & Educators, LLC, a business focused on decreasing healthcare disparities in the United States through education. She is also the founder and leader of LOVED (Ladies of Value Encouragement and Determination), a women's group that supports women's issues in the surrounding community.

In her spare time, Talonda enjoys watching movies and documentaries that focus on black history. Her other hobbies include listening to motivational speakers, reading, singing, and listening to gospel music and oldies from the 50s, 60s, and 70s.

Talonda lives in Coatesville, Pennsylvania, with her husband, Robert, and her children, Sabria, Tayah, Rena, and Cameron.

Learn more at www.riscqhealthcare.com

CPSIA information can be obtained
at www.ICGtesting.com
Printed in the USA
LVHW050204250621
691124LV00002B/259